95

7-CO-ADS 169

JUN 20 '73

67-11665

Flora of the Sea

(Left) *Chrondrus crispus,* a common red seaweed
(Right) A collection of seaweeds growing in a rock pool
at St, Martin's, Isles of Scilly

Flora of the Sea

C. L. DUDDINGTON

THOMAS Y. CROWELL COMPANY
Established 1834
New York

WINGATE COLLEGE LIBRARY
WINGATE, N. C.

First published in the United States of America in 1967
Originally published in Great Britain under the title
Seaweeds and other algae
Copyright © 1966 by C. L. Duddington
All rights reserved. Except for use in a review,
the reproduction or utilization of this work in any form
or by any electronic, mechanical, or other means, now known
or hereafter invented, including photocopying and recording,
and in any information storage and retrieval system is
forbidden without the written permission of the publisher.
Printed in Great Britain
Library of Congress Catalog Card No. 67–11665

Contents

39671

Illustrations

9

TEXT FIGURES

10

Preface

In writing this book I have tried to describe the various kinds of algae in terms that a layman can readily understand. At the same time, I have endeavoured to include enough detail to make the book useful as background reading for the student of elementary Botany. Whether I have succeeded in these two projects, at times diametrically opposed, I leave the reader to judge.

In a work of this kind, which is largely a compilation, it is manifestly impossible to thank personally all the research workers whose work had made the book possible. I should at least, however, like to acknowledge my debt to various standard works on the Algae, and in particular to the following: *The Algae*, by V. J. Chapman; *British Seaweeds*, by Carola Dickinson; *The Structure and Reproduction of the Algae*, by F. E. Fritsch; *Algae and Man*, edited by Daniel F. Johnson; *A Handbook of the British Seaweeds*, by Lily Newton; *Morphologie und Biologie der Algen*, by F. Oltmanns; *The Biology of the Algae*, by F. E. Round; *Cryptogamic Botany*, by Gilbert M. Smith; *Manual of Phycology*, edited by Gilbert M. Smith and *The Algae and their Life Relations*, by Josephine E. Tilden. Without these beacons to guide me I could never have attempted the book. For Chapter 6 the excellent review of the lichens by F. N. Haynes in Volume three of *Viewpoints in Biology* has been an invaluable source of information, and finally I should like to thank Mr. Lawrence D. Hills for his helpful advice when the book was in the planning stage.

I should like to thank Mr. Leo Newman for allowing me to use the photograph of algae growing in a rock pool, reproduced in the frontispiece. The other plates are from photographs in my own collection.

C.L.D.

Kingston-upon-Thames.
1965.

v. dept. still

CHAPTER 1

The first of the plants

In early Palaeozoic times, nearly 500 million years before the
first man began to walk the earth, the sea was already inhabited
by the primitive ancestors of our present-day seaweeds. We have
very little trace of those ancient plants today, for seaweeds,
being composed almost entirely of soft material, do not make
good fossils. We depend upon fossils for our knowledge of plant
life of former times, and where, for any reason, a plant has left
no fossil records behind it, we are left with a blank page in the
history of the plant kingdom.

There is one exception to this. The calcareous seaweeds,
some of which contribute a great deal to the building of coral
reefs in tropical seas, have their soft parts liberally encrusted
with calcium carbonate. The soft parts soon decay, but the
hard skeleton remains as a permanent reminder of what the
plant was like. The calcareous seaweeds, unlike their unprotected brothers, preserved well through the long millennia of
geological time and have left their records in the rocks over
hundreds of millions of years. They tell us that the seaweeds are
very ancient plants.

The algae, then, are primitive plants with a long geological
history behind them. They have altered, of course, with the
passage of hundreds of millions of years, but even today we find
some, like the Cyanophyta or blue-green algae, that are probably
little changed since Palaeozoic times.

Among the algae we include all the seaweeds, but these form
only part of the group. Algae are also found in fresh water,
where they form part of the green scum which can be seen on

13

WINGATE COLLEGE LIBRARY
WINGATE, N. C.

the surface of almost any pond. They are by no means confined to water, however, for they are common in damp soil, and may even be found growing in such dry and inhospitable spots as tree-trunks and old palings. A few are parasitic, and some inhabit the bodies of animals, not as parasites, but as partners for mutual benefit—a condition called symbiosis. Some algae also combine with fungi to form the remarkable plants called lichens.

Algae are simple in structure compared with such intricate organisms as the flowering plants, though some of the larger seaweeds reach a fairly high level of complexity. Their bodies are not divided into root, stem and leaf like those of the higher plants, although in the larger brown seaweeds we may be able to distinguish certain regions, such as a holdfast by which attachment to a rock is secured, a stalk or stipe, and an expanded blade or lamina. The general term 'thallus' is used to describe a simple plant body such as this. Some of the smallest algae consist of only a single microscopic cell. All but a very few contain the green pigment called chlorophyll, characteristic of the leaves of higher plants, which makes it possible for them to build up their organic food from simple inorganic substances by the remarkable process called photosynthesis.

Sometimes the chlorophyll is not obvious. In seaweeds such as the bladderwrack (*Fucus vesiculosus*) that is so common round our coasts the green colour of the chlorophyll is masked by the presence of a brown pigment called fucoxanthin, but leave the seaweed in a bucket of water for a few hours and the green colour will appear in patches as the fucoxanthin is partially washed out.

The algae vary a great deal in size. Some are visible only with the aid of a fairly powerful microscope; single tiny cells that may be motionless or which may swim actively in the water by means of fine, waving 'tails' called flagella, of which there are commonly two. Most algae are of small to moderate size, from the slender filaments of the common algae of fresh water, such as *Spirogyra* and *Zygnema*, to the wracks and ribbon kelps of the seashore. Some algae, on the other hand, reach a considerable size, the fronds of the giant kelp, *Macrocystis*, sometimes attaining 600 feet. Even these giants of the ocean, however, do not attain the bulk of the Douglas fir or the Californian redwood.

If the algae do not grow quite as big as the largest flowering plants, they exceed them very much in their *range* of size; in fact, no other group of plants can approach them. Suppose we could magnify all algae one hundred times. The smallest unicell would then be about a millimetre across—still smaller than the smallest flowering plant. *Macrocystis*, on the other hand, would have a length of 60,000 feet, or nearly twelve miles. Looked at in this way the algae are not to be sneezed at.

In their range of habitat, too, the algae can bear comparison with any other group of plants. The seaweeds are found throughout the oceans of the world, from the equator to near the poles. The larger forms, such as *Macrocystis*, occur in cooler waters, but there is no lack of tropical species to take their place in warmer parts of the world. The number of algae that live in the sea is not always realized, for by far the most numerous are the microscopic unicells that make up the bulk of the floating population known as the plankton. These planktonic algae consist largely of diatoms and dinoflagellates, though other groups are well represented, and their numbers are so colossal as almost to defeat the imagination. The seas cover 71 per cent of the surface of the earth, and almost everywhere they bear a population of millions upon millions of these tiny organisms. It has been calculated that the world production of plankton throughout the year averages about 3·2 tons of dry plankton per acre of sea. Very few land crops can beat this. A good crop of corn, grown under the best conditions, averages about 2·6 tons fresh weight per acre, and even the figure for sugar beet is no more than 13 tons. Of course, the corn is confined to the surface of the earth, whereas the sea is populated in depth; the figures are none the less amazing, however, when we consider the small size of a planktonic organism.

In fresh water algae are scarcely less common than they are in the sea, though owing to the smallness of size of most fresh-water forms they are less conspicuous. There is a fresh-water plankton, corresponding to the marine plankton, consisting of both microscopic and filamentous floating species. Many diatoms and blue-green algae form incrustations on the rocky bottoms of shallower water. Filamentous green algae usually grow attached to submerged objects by their 'holdfast' cells, but may be torn away from their anchorage by wave action and thus join the plankton. In shallow ponds or quiet waters they may form extensive mats floating on the water, and are often given the name 'blanket weed'. The increase in the algal population of swimming-baths and ornamental waters may be a considerable nuisance from time to time.

The algae that grow in hot springs show a remarkable ability to live at temperatures that are lethal to all other plants save certain bacteria. These are mainly blue-green algae, and some of them are capable of secreting either calcium carbonate or silica, forming rock-masses such as travertine and sinter. In some springs the rate at which solid matter is deposited by these algae is phenomenal, reaching a figure as high as 1·5 millimetres in three days. The record for heat tolerance is held by *Phormidium luminosum*, which can live in water at 87·5°C—only 12·5° below the boiling-point. The number of these thermophilic (heat-tolerant) algae is surprisingly large, as many as 53 genera, with 163 species, having been found in Yellowstone Park alone.

Water is not the only medium that can support the growth of algae, for many species have been found in the soil. They occur not only on the surface where there is light, but also at depths where total darkness reigns. Algae cannot grow in the dark, yet in Greenland they have been recovered from the soil to a depth of 40 centimetres. How they get there is still something of a mystery.

Many algae are found growing on tree-trunks, palings, leaves and in other places where the supply of water is tenuous to say the least. A common one is *Pleurococcus*, a unicellular green alga that often forms a green powdery incrustation on the windward side of tree-trunks and walls. As we go from a temperate to a tropical climate the number of these algae increases. Some of the epiphyllous algae (algae that grow on leaves) are

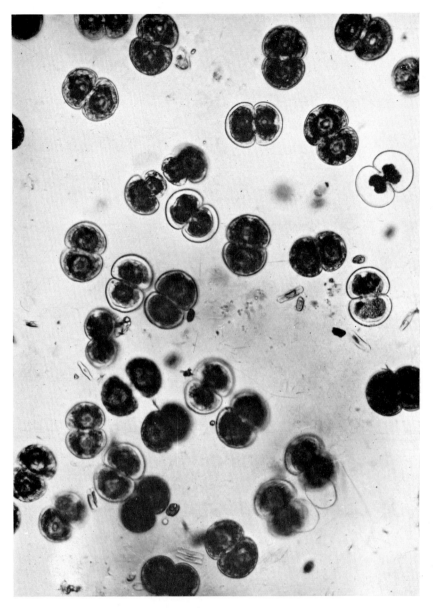

Plate 1. Cosmarium, a placoderm desmid

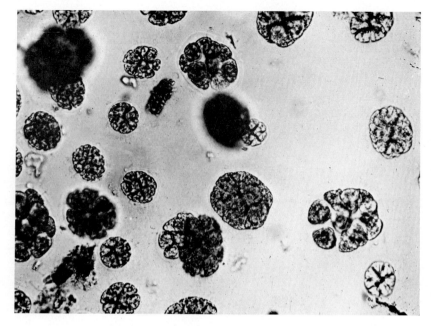

Plate 2. Colonies of *Pandorina*

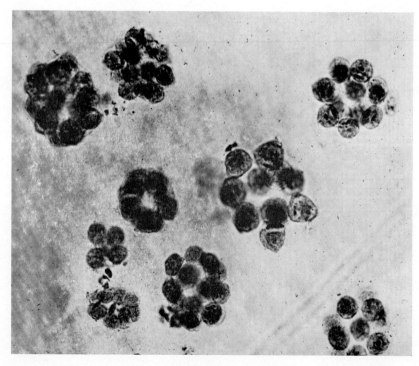

Plate 3. Colonies of *Eudorina*

mere visitors to the surface, but others grow also partly below the surface. When they do this they may become parasitic to a greater or less degree. *Cephaleuros* is a common example, growing in tropical and subtropical regions on the leaves of many plants, including orange, lemon, grapefruit and tea. In India it is particularly common on tea, and is known as 'red rust'.

Those curious plants called lichens are compounded of an alga and a fungus which, so to speak, share the same body. The actual body of the plant is made up of the fungus, but within it are numerous tiny algal cells. There can be little doubt that the fungus profits by the photosynthetic activities of its algal partner, and the algae are dependent on the fungus for their water and mineral salts, since they are not in contact with the ground. The benefits conferred by this partnership must be considerable, for lichens can inhabit the surface of bare rock, as well as living on the tiles of roofs and in other places where it would seem that life would be impossible.

The sharing of a common body by two organisms for material benefit is called symbiosis, from Greek words meaning 'with' and 'life', and is not uncommon in the living world. Algae enter into a number of other symbioses. The marine worm *Convoluta roscoffensis*, for instance, is coloured green by a unicellular alga called *Carteria* that inhabits its body, and the same is true of the fresh-water polyp, *Chlorohydra viridissima*. These algal cells that inhabit the bodies of animals are called zoochlorellae, or when brown instead of green, as they sometimes are, zooxanthellae.

Algae have been put to a number of uses in the past, and their usefulness is increasing, rather than diminishing, as new processes are developed in which algal products play a part. The kelp trade developed in the seventeenth century and until quite recently was an important branch of industry. Brown seaweeds were collected and burned and their ash was used initially as a source of soda. Later it was discovered that it was rich in iodine, and for a long time the iodine of commerce came from seaweed, as it still does in Japan. The discovery of mineral sources of iodine, however, made kelp-burning uneconomic in Europe and America. Seaweeds were also used as a source of potash for a time.

The modern kelp industry seeks a very different product. The recent developments in the use of alginic acid and the alginates for various purposes has led to seaweeds being used for their extraction to an ever-increasing extent. Alginic acid and its products are used in a variety of different ways, from the production of artificial fibres to the making of ice cream, and we have by no means heard the end of the story.

Another material obtained from seaweed is agar-agar. This is used for culturing bacteria and fungi, and has a number of other uses as well, including canning fish, the manufacture of glue and paper, and its pharmaceutical use as a mild laxative. Agar-agar comes mainly from Japan, where it is extracted from the red seaweed *Gelidium amansii*, though during World War II various other sources were developed.

The use of algae as human food has been known through the ages, and, although it has died out in the West, it still flourishes in the Far East, especially China, Japan and Hawaii. In Japan, *Porphyra tenera* is cultivated for food, and various others, especially species of *Laminaria*, *Alaria* and *Arthrothammus*, are also eaten. In recent years much attention has been given to the possibility of growing the unicellular green alga *Chlorella* on a scale that would make it useful as a source of protein in underdeveloped countries, and *Chlorella* 'farms' have been established on a small scale in various countries.

Chlorella has another use. It has been shown that the growth of *Chlorella* in shallow tanks is remarkably efficient in purifying sewage effluents, and the number of sewage farms using *Chlorella* is rapidly on the increase.

One must not forget another time-honoured use of algae— the carting of seaweed in large quantities to fertilize the land. Seaweed makes excellent manure, though its bulk prohibits its being used outside coastal areas, and in these days, when our soil is being starved of humus and poisoned with chemicals, more attention could be given to the enormous store of potential humus to be found in the sea. Seaweeds are also a food for cattle and sheep, and on one of the Orkney Islands there is a race of sheep that is fed entirely on seaweed, apparently without suffering in any way. There is one use for seaweed that far transcends all others. This is the use of the marine plankton in feeding fish. Without it, there would be neither fish nor fisheries. Some fishes feed directly on the plankton, while others, by eating other organisms that are plankton feeders, are just as much dependent on it. If on land it is true to say that all flesh is grass, it is just as true that in the ocean all flesh is plankton.

Algae are classified into a number of groups according to their colour. This is not quite as arbitrary as it may sound, for it has been found that the pigments possessed by algae are a good guide to relationship, and that the algae of a particular colour, whether it be green, brown, red and so on, show various structural and biochemical relationships with one another.

The Chlorophyta are the grass-green algae, for their pigmentation is much the same as that of the higher plants. They also show other points of relationship; thus, they most of them form starch as a result of photosynthesis, and their cell walls contain cellulose. It is thought that somewhere in the Chlorophyta we should seek the origin of the rest of the plant kingdom. Most of the Chlorophyta are fresh-water algae, though a few are marine.

The Euglenophyta are all tiny one-celled creatures that swim with the aid of one or two flagella. These are closely related to the group of simple animals called the Flagellata (Mastigophora); in fact, they cannot be separated from them, and you will find them described in textbooks of zoology as well as in botanical works.

The Chrysophyta is a group that includes three classes: the Xanthophyceae or yellow-green algae, the Chrysophyceae or golden-brown algae, and the Bacillariophyceae or diatoms. They all show an excess of red carotenoid pigments, and starch is lacking, oil being the chief product of photosynthesis. They are all very small. The Xanthophyceae and Chrysophyceae show many signs of a fairly close relationship with one another, but the diatoms, beloved of amateur microscopists on account of their richly ornamental frustules, stand apart.

The Pyrrophyta includes some curious one-celled organisms known to the zoologists as the dinoflagellates. Like the Euglenophyta, this group stands teetering on the line between the plants and the animals, and has members in both camps.

The Phaeophyta are commonly known as the brown algae, for they contain the brown pigment fucoxanthin which masks the green colour of the chlorophyll. All brown algae do not belong to the Phaeophyta, however, for algae of other groups may mimic their brown colour. The Phaeophyta are nearly all marine, and include the largest as well as the commonest of the seaweeds.

The Rhodophyta are the red algae, though they are not always red. They contain the red pigment phycoerythrin and the blue-green pigment phycocyanin, and according to the proportions in which the two pigments are mixed they may be anything from bright red to all the colours of the rainbow. They are an interesting and complex group, showing remarkable uniformity with one another and pronounced differences from other algae. They are particularly abundant in tropical waters, although well represented in temperate seas, and on the whole they are inhabitants of deeper water, seldom appearing in the littoral zone, between the tide marks, unless a rock pool gives them shelter, enabling them to remain submerged even when the tide is out. The Rhodophyta are particularly noteworthy for the complexity of their sexual reproduction, and for the often elaborate structures that are formed after fertilization.

Finally, there are the Cyanophyta, or Myxophyta as they are often called. These are a very ancient group, and many have changed but little, if at all, in more than 500 million years. They are coloured blue-green by the presence in their cells of phycocyanin. They show many differences in organization from the other algae, and are small and of simple structure. Many of them are found in the soil, and a few, such as *Nostoc*, 'fix' atmospheric nitrogen, making it available for the use of other plants.

CHAPTER 2
Mermaid's tresses

One need go no farther than the nearest pond to get algae to look at, for they are all but ubiquitous. Most ponds will produce an abundance of the long, fine green filaments known to some people as 'water silk' or 'mermaid's tresses'. Among these will almost certainly be found *Spirogyra*, one of the commonest fresh-water algae.

Little of the structure of *Spirogyra* can be seen without a microscope, for the filaments are too fine to show detail, even with a hand lens. Under the low power of the microscope, however, *Spirogyra* becomes a thing of beauty. It consists of a row

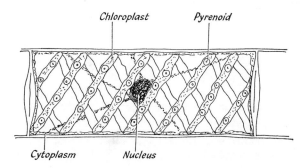

Fig. 1. A cell from a filament of *Spirogyra*.

of box-like cells placed end to end, but what catches the eye at once is the bright green spiral band that seems to run from one end of the filament to the other (Fig. 1). This appearance is deceptive, for the band is not continuous but is broken up in separate portions, of which there may be one, two or several

21

in each cell. These portions are called chloroplasts, and, as we shall see in a moment, they have a most important function in the life of the plant.

The cells of the filament are all similar, and each is surrounded by a cell wall made of thin but fairly rigid material. The cell wall of *Spirogyra* has two layers, the inner one being made of cellulose (the material of cotton and blotting-paper) and the outer one of a substance called pectose.

Cellulose is a carbohydrate and is the material of which the cell walls of most plants are formed. Pectose is also partly a carbohydrate, but it also contains galacturonic acid. With prolonged contact with water it is converted into pectin, a soluble substance that makes the filament of *Spirogyra* feel slimy. As the pectin dissolves away more pectose is formed beneath it.

Inside the cell wall there is a layer of granular, jelly-like material called protoplasm. This is the essential living substance of the cell. It consists of a complex mixture of various substances; proteins, lipoids (fatty materials), sugars, organic acids, mineral salts and various other things. Protoplasm was called by T. H. Huxley 'the physical basis of life', and no more apt description has ever been coined, for the characteristics by which living organisms differ from dead matter depend in the last analysis on the properties of the protoplasm from which they are built.

Living protoplasm is in a constant state of flux, for the many substances that it contains are continually interacting with one another, so that its chemical composition is never quite constant from one moment to the next; in this sense it defies chemical analysis, for before it can be analysed it must first be killed. The chemist can therefore only determine what its composition was at one particular instant in time, and this does not express the state of dynamic equilibrium that is such an important feature of protoplasm when it is alive.

The physical state of living protoplasm is no more constant than its chemical composition. It consists partly of solid material and partly of liquid, the fluid containing the more soluble constituents in solution. Many of the organic compounds of protoplasm are colloids, forming colloidal solutions in water in which the suspended particles are too large to form 'true' solutions. Colloids have certain properties of their own, one of which is the ability to form a jelly in certain circumstances. While the solution is mobile it is called a sol and when it sets it has become a gel. A familiar example is gelatine. It dissolves in hot water to form a sol, and on cooling it sets to a gel. In living protoplasm the colloids are constantly changing from sol to gel and vice versa, and the change from sol to gel, or back again, profoundly alters the properties of the protoplasm and helps to control the activities of the cell.

The protoplasm in a cell of *Spirogyra* forms a lining, so to speak, just inside the cell wall, and encloses a central space filled with fluid. The space is called the vacuole, and the fluid is the cell sap. The liquid cell sap contains many things in solution, such as sugars, organic acids, mineral salts and so on.

The outermost layer of the protoplasm is specially modified to form a very fine membrane, the plasma membrane, and the same is true of the inner edge of the protoplasm, where it lines the vacuole. These membranes are much too fine to be seen with the highest powers of the optical microscope, and until recently we had to rely on the indirect evidence of experiments to know that they were there. In recent years, however, the electron microscope has vastly extended our power of seeing the very small, and we now have direct visual evidence of the existence of these plasma membranes. We can also see that the protoplasm of living cells contains many other, internal, membranes which play an important part in the functioning of the cell. The plasma membranes that form a boundary to the protoplasm are able to control, at least to some extent, the passage of substances into and out of the cell, and it is probable that the internal cell membranes act as surfaces on which chemical reactions can take place.

Somewhere near the middle of the vacuole is a body called the nucleus. This may be regarded as a denser part of the protoplasm, and it is a very important part of the cell. It appears to control the activities of the rest of the protoplasm, and it contains the bodies called chromosomes that carry the genes that determine the hereditary characteristics of the organism. The activities of the nucleus are closely bound up with deoxyribonucleic acid (DNA), which controls the synthesis of protein in cells.

The nucleus is connected with the protoplasm lining the cell wall by slender protoplasmic strands which run across the vacuole. We usually distinguish the part of the protoplasm that is not contained in the nucleus as the cytoplasm.

Spirogyra gets its name from the spirally coiled ribbon-like chloroplasts that run round the cells of the filament, embedded in the cytoplasm, just inside the cell wall. The green colour of the chloroplasts is due to the presence of chlorophyll pigments, of which there are several. The chloroplasts of *Spirogyra* contain chlorophyll *a*, which is bright green in colour, and chlorophyll *b*, which is yellow green. The proportions are about three to one, so that the prevailing colour is grass-green, like all the Chlorophyta—and, incidentally, like the higher plants.

Besides the chlorophylls, the chloroplasts contain other pigments such as yellow xanthophylls and reddish carotenes.

Like all green plants, *Spirogyra* is able to manufacture its own organic food from simple sources—carbon dioxide in the water in which it lives, and simple mineral salts that it also obtains from the water. In the cells of *Spirogyra* carbon dioxide is built into sugar, the other ingredient being water, like this

$$6 \, CO_2 + 12 \, H_2O = C_6H_{12}O_6 + 6 \, O_2 + 6 \, H_2O$$

It may seem a little eccentric to have the symbol H_2O on both sides of the equation, but I have written it in this way to indicate that the oxygen given off as a by-product comes entirely from the water and not from the carbon dioxide.

The miracle represented by this rather prosaic equation is one of the most remarkable processes that Nature has devised. From two very simple substances as a starting-point sugar has been built, and from sugar the plant cell can elaborate any other organic substance that it needs. The process of sugar building requires energy, and this is obtained from light, which is itself a form of energy. To make light energy available to drive this chemical process is the function of the chlorophyll. This substance is able to trap the energy in sunlight and make it available for sugar building. The process is known as photosynthesis, a word which means 'building up by light'.

Photosynthesis is a highly complex process, and the equation that I have given above is a summary of the many reactions that are involved. The first step in the process appears to be the 'fixing' of carbon dioxide: that is, carbon dioxide is combined with some substance already present in the cell. After further changes, light energy is used to break up water molecules, a process called photolysis. This is the source of the oxygen that is given off during photosynthesis. The fixed carbon dioxide is then reduced by hydrogen obtained by the photolysis of water. We are, as yet, uncertain about the initial stages of the process, but the first recognizable photosynthetic substance that we have detected in the cell is phosphoglyceric acid, a compound in which three carbon atoms are combined with hydrogen, oxygen and phosphoric acid. This, by a series of other reactions, gives us sugar.

It is interesting to note that phosphoglyceric acid also appears as one of the intermediate stages of respiration, which is to a certain extent the converse of photosynthesis. In respiration, sugar is oxidized to carbon dioxide and water, like this

$$C_6H_{12}O_6 + 6\ O_2 = 6\ CO_2 + 6\ H_2O$$

Energy is produced, and the cell uses this energy to keep its vital processes going. Like photosynthesis, respiration is a highly complex process, and the equation that I have given is in reality a summary of many separate stages.

Some of the sugar that is formed by photosynthesis is used by the cell for respiration, for respiration is a vital process that must take place constantly, night and day, in all living cells. The amount of sugar that is manufactured in daylight, however, is usually greater than is immediately needed by the plant, and excess sugar is therefore saved up for future use. For storage purposes it is converted into starch. This has the advantage of keeping the reserve carbohydrate in insoluble form, and when more sugar is needed the starch can be quickly broken down into sugar again. Starch consists of small oval grains, and under the microscope each starch grain shows a pattern of rings which are usually not quite concentric.

Close examination of the chloroplast of *Spirogyra* shows that they are studded here and there with small bodies called pyrenoids. These appear to be centres of starch formation, for when the cell is converting sugar into starch the starch grains are first seen forming in the neighbourhood of the pyrenoids, which may become embedded in a mass of starch grains.

The filaments of *Spirogyra* are constantly growing by the formation of new cells, one cell dividing in half and forming new ones. Division of the cell is always preceded by division of the nucleus, one daughter nucleus going to each new cell. The power of division is not confined to any particular cells, so that *Spirogyra* may grow at any point along its length.

Spirogyra reproduces itself in two ways. The simplest method is by the filament breaking in two, each part continuing to grow as a separate plant. This is not quite such a casual process as it sounds. The breaking of the filament is not accidental, but takes place by a definite biological process by which the cell wall between two cells is split. In this process of fragmentation no special reproductive bodies (spores) are formed, and we therefore call it vegetative reproduction. It is comparable with the vegetative reproduction of garden plants through the agency of bulbs, corms, tubers and so on.

Besides reproducing by fragmentation, *Spirogyra* undergoes a process of sexual reproduction, which usually takes place between two filaments that lie side by side. From the cells of each filament small papillae grow out opposite to one another, and as they grow the filaments are pushed apart slightly. The tips of the papillae which are in contact with one another dissolve away, so that a tube called the conjugation tube now connects each pair of opposite cells of the two filaments (Fig. 2). In the cells of one filament the protoplasmic contents contract away from the cell wall, the contraction being brought about by pumping cell sap out of the cells. The pumping action is due to small vacuoles that appear in the cytoplasm, which in-

26

crease in size and then suddenly disappear, discharging their liquid contents outside the cell as they do so. They then re-form and the process is repeated. Because of this pulsating action they are called contractile vacuoles—a term that we shall meet again presently.

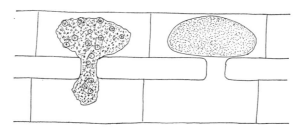

Fig. 2. Part of two conjugating filaments of *Spirogyra*. On the left the contents of the lower (male) cell are just passing into the upper (female) cell. On the right a zygospore is forming.

The contracted contents of the cells of one filament then pass into the conjugation tubes and through them into the opposite filament, the cell contents of which have also contracted to some extent. The mingling of the protoplasm of the two cells (plasmogamy) is then followed by the fusion of the two nuclei (caryogamy), which is the essential part of the sexual process. The cell so formed can be called a zygote, which is the general term for a cell formed as a result of sexual fusion. The zygote surrounds itself with a thick protective cell wall which has two layers; an inner one of cellulose and an outer one which is impregnated with various substances, including a certain amount of waxy material. Any starch that is present is converted into small globules of oil, another form in which food material can be stored up in cells. This thick-walled zygote is called a zygospore.

The type of conjugation process that I have described is called scalariform conjugation, because of the ladder-like appearance of the two filaments joined by their conjugation tubes. There is another type of conjugation where adjoining cells of a filament are concerned, the contents of one cell passing into the

27

next and there forming a zygospore. This is lateral conjugation (Fig. 3).

When the zygospores are set free by the breakdown of the walls of the cells in which they are formed they sink down to the mud at the bottom of the water and remain dormant, like

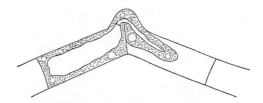

Fig. 3. Lateral conjugation in *Spirogyra.* Note the characteristic geniculate bending of the filament. (Modified, after Lloyd)

seeds, until the time comes for them to germinate. Protected by their tough outer walls they are admirably suited to survive periods of adverse conditions, such as winter frosts or drought, without coming to any harm. When the zygospore finally germinates the young plant that grows out of it remains attached for a time by one end, which is colourless, but after a time it breaks free and the plant floats.

Spirogyra is a very common plant in ponds and lakes and still water generally. Sometimes it forms great masses, covering several acres of water, buoyed up by the oxygen given off during photosynthesis, when it is known as 'blanket weed'—a term that is sometimes applied to other algae that appear in quantity on the top of the water.

Spirogyra belongs to an order of algae called the Conjugales. Many of these are common in ponds and lakes all over the world. They all agree in reproducing by a conjugation process generally similar to that seen in *Spirogyra.*

Zygnema is often found with *Spirogyra.* It consists, like *Spirogyra,* of a filament of box-like cells, but each cell contains two star-shaped chloroplasts with the nucleus of the cell between them (Fig. 4). Another interesting species is *Mougeotia.* This has a single chloroplast in each cell, which is shaped like a flat

28

rectangular plate, with pyrenoids dotted here and there on its surface (Fig. 5). It has the remarkable property of being able to turn about its long axis according to the intensity of the light. In a weak light it places itself so that its flat surface is perpendicular to the direction from which the light is coming, making

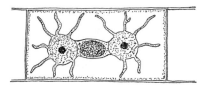

Fig. 4. A cell from a filament of *Zygnema*. Note the two star-shaped chloroplasts with the nucleus between them.

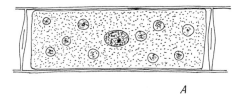

A

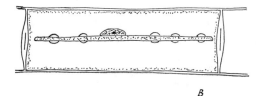

B

Fig. 5. A cell from a filament of *Mougeotia*. In A the flat chloroplast is seen in face view; note the central nucleus and pyrenoids scattered about the surface of the chloroplast. In B the chloroplast is seen in end view. (After Palla)

the best possible use of what light there is for photosynthesis. In a strong light it turns itself edge-on, thereby reducing the amount of light striking the surface. This is sensible behaviour, because very strong light damages chlorophyll.

29

Besides the filamentous algae *Spirogyra* and *Zygnema* the Conjugales include some rather attractive little one-celled plants called desmids. These are of two kinds.

In the placoderm desmids the cell wall is in two parts, and is perforated by many small holes. The common example is *Closterium* (Fig. 6). This consists of a sickle-shaped cell with

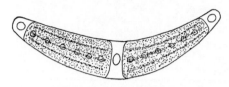

Fig. 6. Closterium, a placoderm desmid.

pointed ends which are often found to contain some crystals of gypsum (calcium sulphate). As far as we know, the gypsum does not play any part in the life of the plant, and is most probably waste matter that the plant has secreted.

The pores that perforate the cell of *Closterium* are neatly arranged in rows, each row being set in a shallow groove. The cells are able to move, and for a long time the method of loco-motion remained a mystery, for *Closterium* has no obvious organs of movement such as the flagella possessed by many one-celled algae. We now know *Closterium* moves by a kind of natural jet-propulsion, a treacly fluid called mucilage being exuded through some rather larger pores at the ends of the cell.

Fig. 7. Spirotaenia, a saccoderm desmid. Note the spirally coiled chloro-plast, like that of *Spirogyra*.

It is an interesting thought that jet-propulsion arrived on the earth long before the wheel.

The saccoderm desmids also consist of single cells, but here the cell wall is quite smooth and not perforated by pores. Some of the saccoderm desmids mimic the filamentous Conjugales in the form of their chloroplasts; in *Spirotaenia*, for instance, the chloroplast is a spirally twisted ribbon like that of *Spirogyra* (Fig. 7). The saccoderm desmids do not have the power of movement by jet-propulsion possessed by the placoderm desmids.

CHAPTER 3

From unicell to colony

Sometimes after rain the puddles are coloured a beautiful bright green. This rather pleasant phenomenon is due to the multiplication in the puddles of a minute green alga called *Chlamydomonas*, one of the smallest of the algae. There are about 350 different species, but most of them are similar in structure. A single individual *Chlamydomonas* is so small that it can only be seen with a microscope, but when they multiply in thousands, in a rain puddle or in the water in a ditch or a pond, they may be so numerous that they give the water a green colour.

Chlamydomonas consists of only a single cell, but in that cell is contained all the essential attributes of a complete plant. It is usually egg-shaped, one end being somewhat pointed. From the pointed end sprout two very fine protoplasmic 'tails', which by their waving movements enable the tiny organism to swim actively in the water in which it lives (Fig. 8). They are called flagella, from the Latin word *flagellum*, meaning a whip. When the organism is swimming the flagella move in a similar way to the arms of a person swimming breast-stroke; they sweep stiffly backwards, drawing the cell through the water, and then, relaxing, they move forwards, offering as little resistance as possible, ready for another stroke.

The most conspicuous object in the *Chlamydomonas* cell is a large green chloroplast. The form of this varies from species to species, but it is usually cup-shaped, and it is situated at the hinder end of the cell, of which it occupies more than half. The remainder of the cell is occupied by the living protoplasm, and this contains a nucleus, which is usually partly hidden in the

32

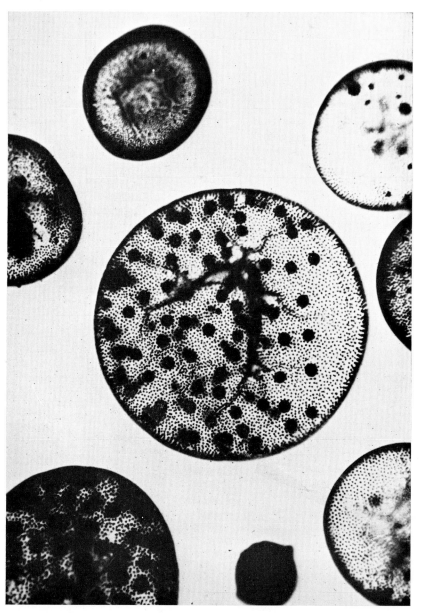

Plate 4. Colonies of *Volvox*

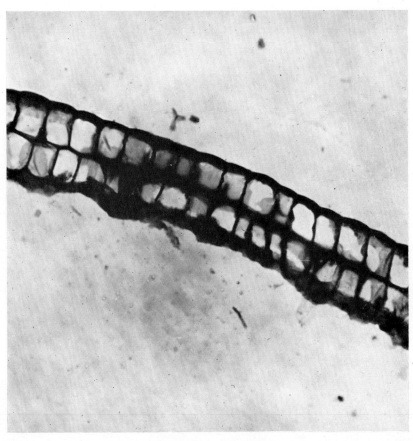

Plate 5. Section through part of the thallus of *Ulva.* Note the cells arranged in two layers

cup formed by the chloroplast. On one side of the chloroplast there is usually a pyrenoid, similar to those found in *Spirogyra*. Some species of *Chlamydomonas* have more than one pyrenoid, and may even have more than one chloroplast.

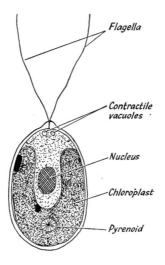

Fig. 8. Chlamydomonas.

The twin flagella grow out from the pointed end of the cell, and at the base of each is a small solid body called the blepharoplast, which appears to have some controlling influence on the action of the flagellum to which it is attached. Also at the pointed end of the cell are two small circular vacuoles. These are in a constant state of expansion and contraction; watching them under a powerful microscope we can see that each vacuole increases in size to a certain point, and then suddenly disappears; this process of gradual expansion and sudden contraction is constantly repeated, and the movement of the two vacuoles alternates. Because of this pulsating action they are called contractile vacuoles. Their function appears to be the elimination of water. The cells are constantly taking in water, and if there were no means of getting rid of it the cell would soon be in trouble. The contractile vacuoles act in the same way as the bilge pump of a ship. It is also possible that some of the waste products formed by the cell are got rid of with the water that is forced out by the contractile vacuoles, which then act as organs of excretion as well as water regulators.

The cell of *Chlamydomonas* is surrounded by a very thin cell wall made of cellulose. There may also be an outer layer of pectose, as in *Spirogyra*, which adds a slimy coat to the cell.

At one side of the cell there is a tiny spot of bright red pigment called the pigment spot, or, rather less accurately, the 'eye spot', and experiments have shown that it enables the cell to react to light. *Chlamydomonas* needs light for photosynthesis, though, like *Mougeotia*, it avoids over-illumination because of its harmful effect. We find, therefore, that *Chlamydomonas* usually swims towards moderate light, but away from very bright light. Even such a small creature 'knows' what is good for it.

Chlamydomonas is able to multiply very quickly by a process which, because sex is not involved, is called asexual reproduction. The contents of a cell divide lengthways into two equal portions, and these divide again lengthways into four. Each of these portions becomes a small individual, complete with chloroplast, flagella, and so on (Fig. 9). The old cell wall breaks down

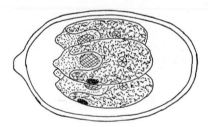

Fig. 9. Chlamydomonas: cell after undergoing division into four zoöspores.

and these zoöspores, as they are called, are set free in the water, when each grows into a new *Chlamydomonas* cell. Usually each reproducing cell forms four zoöspores, but in some species of *Chlamydomonas* the number is two, and in others may be eight.

Sometimes when a *Chlamydomonas* cell divides the daughter

cells do not develop flagella and become zoöspores, but instead they in turn divide while still enclosed in the wall of the parent cell. This process may be repeated many times, the old cell walls gradually becoming soft and gelatinous, so that finally a mass of cells is formed. This is known as the palmella state, and the masses of cells that are thus formed may be quite large. Eventually the mass of cells breaks up into individuals, which grow flagella and become normal *Chlamydomonas* cells.

The process of asexual reproduction makes it possible for *Chlamydomonas* to multiply very quickly when living conditions are good. It is, however, not the only reproductive process available to this simple yet beautifully constructed little organism. *Chlamydomonas* also undergoes sexual reproduction, the details of which vary in different species. The contents of a cell divide lengthways into eight, sixteen, or thirty-two portions, all of which are similar to, though smaller than, the zoöspores formed during the asexual reproduction. These cells are sex cells or gametes; they are set free in the water by the breaking down of the old cell wall, and they come together in pairs. Usually the flagella of a conjugating pair of gametes become intertwined, and the two gametes, after dancing around for a time, gradually fuse with one another, forming a fusion cell or zygote. The flagella of the two gametes remain separate and do not cease to operate, so that at first the newly formed zygote swims around with four flagella (Fig. 10). Eventually, however, the zygote withdraws its flagella, adopts a more or less spherical shape, and surrounds itself with a thick cell wall. It is now called a zygospore. The protoplasm of the zygospore often develops a red pigment called haematochrome, giving the whole cell a reddish colour. Protected by its thick outer wall, the zygospore is able to withstand adverse conditions that would kill a normal active cell; it is unharmed, for instance, if the water in which it was formed should happen to dry up. In dry conditions zygospores of *Chlamydomonas* may be blown from place to place by the wind, or even carried on the feet of birds, thus securing the dispersal of the organisms. Eventually the zygospore germinates, its contents dividing up to form zoöspores, which are set free

35

by the breaking down of the thick outer covering and then grow into new individuals.

When *Chlamydomonas* reproduces sexually the two gametes that fuse are precisely similar to one another. It is therefore impossible to speak of one as male and the other as female. It

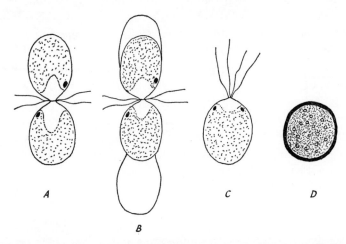

Fig. 10. Sexual reproduction in *Chlamydomonas*. In A, two individuals have approached one another. In B, each is slipping out of its old cell wall (in some species of *Chlamydomonas* the cell wall is absent). C, zygote with four flagella, after conjugation. D, resting zygospore.

has been observed, however, that in many species of *Chlamydomonas* the two gametes that fuse originate from different individuals, and this indicates that there is some invisible difference between one individual and another which determines whether or not the gametes they produce can fuse with one another. It has been shown that these species of *Chlamydomonas* exist in two types or strains, called respectively the plus and minus strains. A gamete from a plus individual will fuse only with one from a minus individual, and vice versa. This phenomenon is known as heterothallism, and it must not be confused with sex, although it is probably something akin to it. Heterothallism is very common in the lower plants, and especially in the fungi.

The gametes that fuse are not always similar. *Chlamydomonas*

36

braunii is unusual in that it produces two kinds of gametes, those from some individuals being large while those from others are small. In *C. braunii* we find that fusion always takes place between a large and a small gamete. It is possible to regard a large gamete as being female and the small gamete as male.

Chlamydomonas oogamum goes much further than this, for the female individuals each produce a single large gamete which has no flagella. This large gamete or egg cell is set free into the water and is fertilized by a small motile male gamete of the usual kind.

Chlamydomonas may be taken as the starting-point of a whole series of algae in which a number of cells, each essentially similar to *Chlamydomonas*, are joined together to form a compound structure, known as a colony. These colonial algae vary in size and complexity, from small colonies consisting of only a few cells to the very large colonies of *Volvox*, in which some thousands of cells are grouped together to form a spherical colony big enough to be seen by the naked eye.

Gonium is one of the simplest of these colonial forms. The commonest species, *G. pectorale*, consists of sixteen cells, arranged in the form of a slightly curved plate. The cells are symmetrically arranged, four in the centre and twelve round the edge, with their flagella directed outwards, and the whole colony is surrounded with a gelatinous material that helps to keep it together (Fig. 11). The colony swims by the united action of all its flagella, slowly spinning round as it does so.

Each cell in a *Gonium* colony is built on the same plan as an individual of *Chlamydomonas*. Besides a pair of flagella, it has the usual cup-shaped chloroplast, a red eye spot, and the pair of contractile vacuoles that we find in *Chlamydomonas*. Each cell is an individual in itself, for although the sixteen cells are joined together by sticky mucilage, their personalities are not merged together. That is why an arrangement of this kind is called a colony rather than an individual.

Gonium reproduces asexually and sexually in much the same way as *Chlamydomonas*. When zoöspores are formed in asexual reproduction, all sixteen cells of a colony produce their

37

zoöspores simultaneously. Each zoöspore will give rise to a new colony, dividing up to form sixteen cells. Similarly, when sexual reproduction takes place, two gametes fuse to form a zygote, which, as in *Chlamydomonas*, has at first four flagella. Presently the zygote withdraws its flagella and forms a zygospore, and

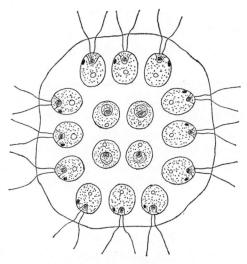

Fig. 11. Sixteen-celled colony of *Gonium*. (After Hartmann)

when the time comes for this to germinate its contents divide up to form a small colony of four cells, which is then set free in the water by the breaking down of the outer wall of the zygospore. The four cells of this colony then divide further to give rise to the usual colony of sixteen cells.

Pandorina is another common colonial alga related to *Chlamydomonas*. A colony of *Pandorina*, instead of being platelike as in *Gonium*, is spherical, and may consist of four, eight, sixteen, or thirty-two cells, according to the species; in the commonest species, *P. morium*, there are sixteen cells (Fig. 12). As in *Gonium*, the colony is surrounded by gelatinous material.

The cells of a *Pandorina* colony are essentially similar to *Chlamydomonas*, and, as in *Gonium*, are arranged with their flagella pointing outwards, so that the colony is able to swim

38

by their combined movement. As before, all the cells of the colony take part in both asexual and sexual reproduction.

In *Gonium* and *Pandorina* all the cells of the colony are similar to one another, and all have the power of reproduction. In larger colonial algae this is not so, for, as the colonies get

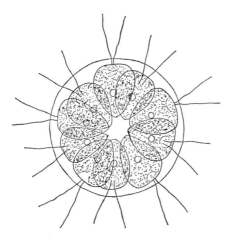

Fig. 12. Spherical colony of *Pandorina.*

bigger, we find the important principle called division of labour becoming apparent; instead of all the cells being similar, both structurally and functionally, certain parts of the colony have special functions of their own. The simplest instance of this can be seen in *Eudorina.* This consists of small spherical or ellipsoidal colonies similar in construction to those of *Pandorina,* but rather larger, being made up of sixteen, thirty-two, or sixty-four cells. In most species of *Eudorina* all the cells are similar, but in *E. illinoiensis* four cells at the front end of the colony are very much smaller than the rest, and take no part in reproduction (Fig. 13). These four cells have lost the capacity to reproduce; they are purely vegetative cells, and they represent the first inkling of a development of a soma, or vegetative plant body, as distinct from the reproductive body. This is a very important step forward in evolution, for without it the development of a complex plant such as is seen in the larger algae, or in the

39

higher plants, would have been impossible. As long as every cell in the plant is compelled to retain the reproductive function, specialization of different tissues for different purposes remains impossible, but the development of somatic cells, as distinct from reproductive cells, made it possible for plants to evolve

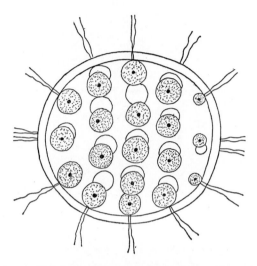

Fig. 13. Colony of *Eudorina illinoiensis.* Note the small vegetative cells at one end. (After Kofoid)

highly organized bodies built up of various tissues, each serving a particular function in the life of the plant.

E. illinoiensis, with its four somatic cells, is a long way from developing the complex structure that is seen, for instance, in some of the brown algae. Nevertheless, this little plant has made one of the most significant steps forward in the whole great panorama of evolution.

The development of a soma is taken a step further in *Pleodorina.* This alga is very like *Eudorina,* but larger, its spherical colonies consisting of 32, 64, or 128 cells. In *Pleodorina,* however, the somatic cells assume greater importance, for there are more of them; in some species they may occupy more than half the total area of the colony.

40

We come now to the largest and most complex, as well as the best known, of the colonial algae related to *Chlamydomonas*. This is *Volvox*, a name derived from the Latin word *volvere*, meaning 'to roll'. *Volvox* forms huge colonies, each consisting of from 500 to 60,000 cells, the number varying between different species. The colony is spherical, and its whole interior is filled with sticky mucilage in some species, such as *V. aureus*, or with water in others, such as the well-known *V. globator*.

Each cell of a *Volvox* colony has a pair of flagella and the whole colony swims, turning over as it does so like a ball rolling. In most species of *Volvox* the cells are not isolated from one another, but are connected by fine strands of protoplasm called plasmodesmata. These protoplasmic connexions between the cells no doubt help to co-ordinate the activities of the individual cells of a colony—an important point where the colonies are so large.

In *Volvox* nearly all the cells of a colony are somatic, the reproductive function being confined to a few cells scattered here and there. The asexual reproductive cells are called gonidia, and there are normally between two and fifty of them in a colony. When asexual reproduction begins a gonidium divides again and again as a result of which a little sphere is formed. The sphere projects into the interior of the mother colony, and at the end at which it is attached there is an opening called the phialopore. The cells of the sphere are oval in outline and their pointed ends are directed inwards, but presently a curious thing happens. The sphere turns itself inside out through its own phialopore, so that we now have the pointed ends of the cells directed outwards. The cells develop flagella, and the new daughter colony is set free to begin life on its own.

In the larger species of *Volvox* the daughter colonies are liberated inside the parent colony, where they live for a time. They are not set free from confinement until the death of the parent colony, which then breaks up and allows their escape.

The sexual reproductive organs of *Volvox* are initially cells that look very much like gonidia. The male reproductive cell divides up to form from 16 to 512 male gametes, each of which has a pair of flagella that enable it to swim. The female reproductive cell does not divide, but instead it loses its flagella and its contents swell somewhat, forming a spherical egg cell. Male gametes seek out the egg cells, probably attracted to them by some chemical substance that the egg cells produce, and a male gamete penetrates the gelatinous envelope that surrounds the egg, and, burrowing into the egg, fertilizes it. When the egg has been fertilized it surrounds itself with a thick wall, which may be smooth or spiny, and turns orange-red in colour owing to the development of a haematochrome pigment. It is called an oöspore instead of a zygospore, because the female cell is a non-motile egg cell. Eventually it is set free from the colony and, after a fairly prolonged dormant period, it germinates. Its outer wall splits and its inner wall becomes puffed out like a bubble, forming what is called a vesicle. Inside this the protoplasm of the oöspore divides up to form a colony, in much the same way as a colony is formed from a gonidium. This new colony is, however, a small one, consisting of not more than 256 cells. The small colony soon reproduces asexually, forming a somewhat larger colony, and this process is repeated for half a dozen generations or so until a colony of normal size is produced.

Volvox is at the pinnacle of its own particular line of evolution. The colonial algae that we have so far considered, together with certain others that we have not mentioned, form an order called the Volvocales. Starting from *Chlamydomonas*, the Volvocales show progressively increasing complexity, accompanied by increase in size, but in *Volvox* the limit is reached. A colonial structure of this kind does not lend itself to a development of a highly complex organization, and with each cell retaining so much individuality there is little scope for the development of division of labour, such as may be seen in the higher algae. *Volvox* has a well-developed soma, for the reproductive function has been relegated to a mere handful of cells in a colony in which there are several thousands, but the colonial structure is not sufficiently plastic to allow further splitting up of the soma into various parts, each specialized to perform a particular function. The colonial line comes to a dead end in *Volvox*.

CHAPTER 4

A digression on the nucleus

In Chapter 2 I indicated that the nucleus is a specially important part of the cell, and that it exerts a controlling influence on the cytoplasm outside. It is time we had a closer look at the nucleus, for without a little understanding of how it works it will be difficult to follow the life histories of some of the more complex algae.

The nucleus is a very uniform structure throughout the plant kingdom if we except those two very primitive groups, the bacteria and the Cyanophyta. Its particular significance is that it is the home of the deoxyribonucleic acid, or DNA, that plays such a vital part in the proper functioning, as well as the reproduction, of all living cells. The nucleus has two major functions to perform. It has to control the activities of the cytoplasm and in particular to superintend the synthesis of new protein in the cell. It also has to pass on hereditary information from mother cell to daughter cell when cell division takes place, making sure that the right kind of cell is formed. We do not expect a cow to have a litter of kittens, nor do we expect a colony of *Volvox* to emerge from a germinating zygospore of *Spirogyra*. It is the DNA in the nucleus that sees to it that we are not disappointed.

The molecule of DNA is highly complex, consisting of thousands of units placed one behind another in a long chain. The units themselves are not atoms, but molecules containing many atoms. What we may term the 'backbone' of the chain consists of phosphate groups alternating with molecules of a sugar, deoxyribose. Each sugar molecule has, sticking out from it, what is called a 'side chain', which is a purine base. There are two phosphate-sugar chains in the DNA molecule and they are wound round one another in a loose spiral.

There are only four different kinds of base found in DNA, and these are adenine, guanine, cytosine and uracil. The length of the chain is so great, however, that these four occur many thousands of times. The order in which they are placed on the DNA chain forms a sort of code, which can be read in terms of amino-acid molecules, and amino-acids are the bricks out of which proteins are built. A protein molecule consists of a long chain of amino-acids joined together. There are about twenty different amino-acids that commonly go to make up proteins, though a given protein may not have them all. A protein may contain many hundreds of amino-acids in its molecule, so that, according to the order in which they are arranged, we have the possibility of an almost infinite number of different proteins.

Let us get back to our code. The DNA code can be likened to the Morse code, if it could be imagined that the letters of the Morse code all had three symbols. Thus, when a wireless operator sends 'dot-dot-dot dash-dash-dash dot-dot-dot' the hearer reads it as 'SOS'. Similarly, when the sequence of bases on the DNA chain is adenine-cytosine-adenine it represents asparagine, or when it goes uracil-uracil-uracil it means phenylalanine. Asparagine and phenylalanine are just two of the amino-acids that make up proteins. You can see now how the DNA molecule, with its long chain, can spell out the amino-acids, in their right order, that go to make up a protein molecule.

We have, however, only begun to solve the difficulty of the syntheses of proteins in cells, for the proteins are manufactured in the cytoplasm, while the DNA is in the nucleus. How does the DNA control protein-building at a distance? How is the information contained in its code transported intact to the centres of protein manufacture in the cell?

The answer lies in another form of nucleic acid called ribonucleic acid or RNA. The DNA acts as a template, as it were, for the manufacture of a RNA molecule in the nucleus, and impresses upon it that part of the code which is necessary for the formation of a particular protein. The RNA molecule bearing the information then passes out of the nucleus and acts as a template for the assembly of a protein molecule, all the right amino-acids being put together in their right order.

Of course, there are many added complications in the very complex story of protein synthesis. There are, for instance, several kinds of RNA, such as messenger RNA which carries the information out of the nucleus, transfer RNA which rounds up the correct amino-acids and brings them to the site of protein synthesis, and so on. The work on DNA and RNA has all been done within the last few years, and we are only at the beginning of the story as yet.

The DNA molecule has not only to direct the synthesis of proteins in the cell that it occupies, but it must also be self-reproducing so that it can be passed on to the new cells that are formed on cell division. When a cell divides, therefore, the DNA in its nucleus must act as a template for the formation of another molecule of DNA bearing the same code as itself. This it does.

When a cell is not dividing its nucleus is sometimes said to be 'resting'—a thoroughly bad term, for it is really extremely active, as we have seen. It is far better to speak of the nucleus as being in its 'metabolic state'. A metabolic nucleus appears as a spherical or ovoid body surrounded by a nuclear membrane. We can see little of the contents of the nucleus even with appropriate staining techniques, for the stain does not 'take', but a conspicuous feature of most nuclei is a small, densely staining body called the nucleolus. Sometimes there are more than one.

When the nucleus is about to divide the nuclear membrane disappears, the nucleolus gradually loses its stainability, and at the same time a number of rod-like bodies appear. These are the chromosomes, and they are the home of the DNA. The chromosomes vary a great deal in length and shape from one another, but a set of chromosomes from any cell of any plant *of the same species* will always be the same in shape and in number. Moreover, they are in pairs, each member of a pair being identical with its fellow. The two chromosomes of a pair are said to be homologous.

45

Careful examination of the chromosomes when they appear at the onset of cell division shows that each one is split lengthways into two exactly similar halves, called chromatids, which are joined together at a point called the spindle attachment.

As the division proceeds a number of lines appear in the cytoplasm, making a barrel-shaped figure which is called the spindle. The chromosomes arrange themselves in a ring round the equator of the spindle, and then the two chromatids of which each chromosome is composed break apart and one travels to each pole of the spindle. We have now, at the poles of the spindle, two identical sets of chromatids, soon to become chromosomes in their own right. The chromatids now gradually lose their stainability, nucleoli and nuclear membranes are formed, and we have two nuclei where we formerly had one. There only remains a cell wall to be formed, which in most plant cells is constructed across the equator of the spindle, and division of the cell is complete.

This process is called mitosis. Essentially it is a means of securing the exact partition of the DNA between the two new nuclei, so that each nucleus receives exactly the same share as the other. Remember that the misplacement of a single base among the thousands on a DNA chain might mean the death of the cell, and you will realize how important this is.

The number of chromosomes in the nucleus varies from a few in some plants to many in others, but for a given species of plant it is always the same (I am not concerned here with the phenomenon that the geneticist calls polyploidy, which is another story). From what I have said about the activities of DNA it is fairly obvious that this must be so. Every species has its own chromosome number, which does not change from one generation to the next.

When we come to sexual reproduction a complication is introduced, for two sex cells or gametes fuse to form a zygote, their nuclei also fusing. It is the fusion of the two parental nuclei that is the essence of the sexual act. Now, when the two nuclei fuse their chromosomes retain their individuality, so that the zygote nucleus has a double set of chromosomes. How is it,

46

then, that the chromosome number of a species remains constant, in spite of being doubled every time sexual reproduction takes place?

The answer to this apparent paradox lies in the behaviour of the chromosomes. Some time before sexual reproduction takes place the chromosome number is halved, so that when the gametes fuse the chromosome number for the species is not doubled, but merely restored. The nuclear division that brings this about is called meiosis.

Meiosis differs from mitosis in several ways, but the essential point is this. When the chromosomes are assembled on the equator of the spindle they are arranged in homologous pairs— remember that every chromosome has its homologue. When the time comes for the movement towards the poles of the spindle, instead of the chromosomes breaking into their chromatids it is *one member of each homologous pair* that travels to opposite poles of the spindle. You see what has happened. Instead of having a pair of each kind of chromosome, each daughter nucleus now has only one. Its chromosome number has been halved, yet we still have two identical—or apparently identical —daughter nuclei. Actually there are genetic differences between the two chromosomes of a homologous pair that cannot be seen under the microscope, but these need not concern us.

A cell or an organism that contains two members of each homologous pair of chromosomes in its nuclei is said to be diploid. When its chromosome number has been halved by meiosis it is called haploid. Most animals are diploid, meiosis occurring when the gametes are formed. The higher plants are also diploid. Simple plants like the algae, however, may be diploid or haploid, according to where meiosis occurs in the life history. All the algae that I have so far dealt with are haploid, for meiosis occurs when the zygote germinates to form a new plant, the only diploid cell being the zygote itself. This is far from being the case with all algae, however, as we shall see. In many algae there is even an alternation between a haploid and a diploid generation, the one following the other with clockwork regularity.

All this arises from the necessity of exactly splitting the DNA in the nucleus, for DNA is the essential substance on which life depends. Samuel Butler once said that a hen is an egg's way of making another egg; a biologist might say that an organism is DNA's way of making some more DNA.

CHAPTER 5

Various green algae

In the second chapter I described some filamentous green algae belonging to the order Conjugales, of which *Spirogyra* is the most familiar example. The filamentous habit is by no means confined to these, for it is extremely common in the algae and is found in a number of different groups. Some of these, in addition to filamentous species, also contain parenchymatous forms: algae in which the cells divide in more than one plane, producing a flat expanded thallus instead of a filament. The order Ulotrichales is one of these.

Ulothrix is an important genus containing about thirty species, most of which are found in fresh water. The common *U. zonata* seems to have a definite liking for cold water, for it usually makes its appearance early in the spring, multiplies rapidly for a time, and then all but disappears as spring merges into summer, to appear again in the autumn as the water cools down. *Ulothrix*, like *Spirogyra*, has the form of a long filament made up of rectangular cells, each containing a single large chloroplast which in *Ulothrix* is like a circular band round the cell (Fig. 14). The filament of *Ulothrix* is usually attached to some solid body in the water, the end cell being specially modified to form a holdfast, and this cell is often without chlorophyll. Often, however, the filaments eventually break away and float freely in the water.

Ulothrix can reproduce vegetatively by fragmentation, parts of the filament breaking off and growing into new plants. It also reproduces asexually by means of zoöspores, which may be formed in any of the cells of the filament. The number of zoöspores formed by a particular cell appears to depend on its width; a wide cell may produce from two to thirty-two, the number usually being a power of two, while a narrow cell can only manage one or two, or at most four. Zoöspores of *Ulothrix* have four flagella instead of the usual two. Sometimes zoöspores

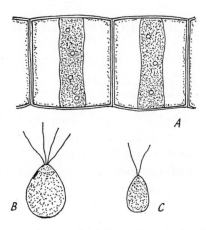

Fig. 14. A, part of a filament of *Ulothrix*. Note the band-like chloroplast round the middle of the cell. B, a zoöspore with four flagella. C, a biflagellate gamete.

fail to grow flagella and they are then called aplanospores, a general term used for a non-motile spore.

Sexual reproduction in *Ulothrix* takes place by the joining together of motile gametes which, unlike zoöspores, have only two flagella. They are formed in a similar way to the zoöspores.

An interesting and very familiar member of the Ulotrichales is *Ulva*, the sea lettuce. This is one of the commonest seaweeds round our coasts. It is usually found in rock pools between the tide marks, especially in water that is polluted by sewage. It consists of a thin bright green thallus very much like a lettuce leaf, attached at one end to a stone or to the rock wall of the pool (Fig. 15).

The thallus of *Ulva* forms a sheet two cells thick, and it is attached to the substratum by a definite holdfast consisting of root-like outgrowths. Each cell contains a single large chloro-

50

plast and a single nucleus; usually the chloroplast is placed towards the outer side of the cell and the nucleus towards the inner side.

Ulva has an interesting life history in which asexual and sexual reproduction alternate. Asexual reproduction takes place

Fig. 15. Thallus of *Ulva lactuca.*

as in *Ulothrix.* The contents of some of the cells divide up, usually into four or eight portions, each of which becomes a zoöspore with four flagella. The zoöspores escape into the water through an opening in the wall of the cell in which they were formed, and, after swimming around for some time, they settle and germinate. When a zoöspore germinates it first divides into two cells, one of which forms the holdfast while the other grows out into a filament consisting of cells arranged in a single row, as in a filament of *Ulothrix.* Presently, however, the cells of the filament begin to divide in more than one direction, so that a flat sheet of cells is formed. This grows into the familiar green leaf-like thallus of *Ulva.*

The new thallus closely resembles the old one that gave rise to the zoöspores, but it differs from it in one important point.

Instead of producing zoöspores, it produces gametes by which sexual reproduction is brought about. These are formed in a similar way to the zoöspores, but they are smaller, each cell producing either thirty-two or sixty-four of them, and they have only two flagella. The gametes join together in pairs, forming zygotes, each of which has four flagella. The zygotes are at first attracted by moderate light, but after a time they begin to be repelled by light, and so swim deeper into the water, towards the bottom. A zygote settles on some solid object and germinates in the same way as a zoöspore, producing a filament which later expands to become a flat thallus. The plant produced by the germination of the zygote reproduces asexually, by means of zoöspores, to produce more plants that form gametes and reproduce sexually. There is thus a regular alternation between asexual and sexual generations, the asexual generation producing zoöspores while the sexual generation produces gametes.

In *Ulva* meiosis occurs when the zoöspores are formed. The asexual generation is therefore diploid, while the sexual generation is haploid. Because the two generations are exactly alike in appearance the alternation of generations is said to be isomorphic.

Ulva lactuca is sometimes known as the green laver. It is edible, and used at one time to appear at dinner parties as a substitute for the purple laver (*Porphyra umbilicalis*), though it is not so good. It is collected by fishermen from the coast of China to be sold both as a food and as a medicine to combat fevers.

Enteromorpha is another very common green seaweed belonging to the same family as *Ulva*, and it, too, has an isomorphic alternation of generations. The thallus of *Enteromorpha* is built up, like that of *Ulva*, of two layers of cells, but whereas in *Ulva* the two layers remain pressed together throughout the life of the plant, in *Enteromorpha* they separate from one another so that they form a tube half an inch or so in diameter. *Enteromorpha* gets its name from its fancied resemblance to an intestine (Fig. 16).

Enteromorpha is often found growing in the upper part of the littoral zone—the zone between high and low tide marks—and it is particularly common in places where streams of fresh water dash down the cliffs and wander over the rocks to the sea. Some species of *Enteromorpha* are, in fact, found in fresh waters. The same kind of tendency is also seen in *Ulva*, for, though this is a

Fig. 16. Thallus of *Enteromorpha intestinalis.*

purely marine genus, it is very tolerant of variations in the salinity of the water in which it is growing, and in estuaries it may grow in waters that are brackish rather than salt.

Enteromorpha reproduces both asexually and sexually in a similar way to *Ulva*. There is a strong tendency, however, for the gametes of *Enteromorpha* to vary in size, and in the common *E. intestinalis* we always have fusion between a relatively large female gamete, with a bright green chloroplast, and a smaller, narrower male gamete in which the chloroplast is a pale yellowish-green colour. In *E. intestinales* it is even possible to distinguish the male from the female plants by their appearance, for in the male plant the fertile portions, where thc gametes are produced, are orange-yellow in colour, showing up distinctly against the green of the rest of the thallus, while in the female plant the fertile areas are yellowish-green and not so easily distinguished. In *Enteromorpha*, as in *Ulva*, the sexual plants are haploid, while the asexual plants are diploid.

In China and Japan *Enteromorpha* is commonly eaten, but its use as a food does not seem to have extended to the West.

Enteromorpha has an important connexion with the development on rocks of the large brown seaweeds known as wracks, such as the bladderwrack (*Fucus vesiculosus*). The young plants of *Fucus* develop best on rocks that are covered with a soft felt of *Enteromorpha*. If large numbers of limpets (*Patella*) are present they will eat most of the *Enteromorpha*, to which they are much addicted, and that, in turn, will make it difficult for *Fucus* to establish itself. Relationships like this are very common in Nature, and sometimes they can be extremely complex. The most famous is the connexion, first pointed out by Darwin, between cats and clover. The flowers of clover, with their long corolla tubes, can be pollinated only by humble-bees. The nests of humble-bees are destroyed by field mice, which, in turn, are preyed on by cats. Clover, therefore, thrives in districts where cats are plentiful.

Leaving the Ulotrichales, we come now to a small but important order of filamentous algae called the Oedogoniales. This little order contains only three genera—*Oedogonium*, *Oedocladium*, and *Bulbochaete*. The principal character that separates these three genera from other algae is the fact that their zoöspores and gametes, instead of having two or four flagella, are provided with a whole ring of flagella round one end. On account of this curious type of flagellation they were formerly placed by themselves in a group called the Stephanokontae. They have also, as we shall see in a moment, an extraordinary method of cell division which is unique in the plant kingdom. All three genera are found in fresh water.

Oedogonium is one of the commonest of the fresh-water algae and a search in any pond will almost certainly produce some specimens. It is sometimes found in running water, but this habitat does not really suit it.

Oedogonium forms long slender filaments which are just about visible to the naked eye. It is not free-floating, but normally grows attached to some solid body, such as a submerged stone or a water plant. As the filaments grow older, however, they tend to break away and float in the water.

The filament of *Oedogonium* consists, as in other filamentous algae, of rectangular cells placed end to end. Each cell contains a single chloroplast, which is in the form of a cylindrical network lying in the cytoplasm of the cell, just inside the cell wall (Fig. 17). Here and there on the chloroplast there are pyrenoids.

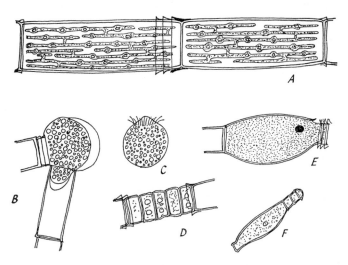

Fig. 17. Oedogonium. A, two cells from the filament, one a cap cell. B, emission of zoöspore. C, zoöspore. D, row of antheridia. E, oögonium. F, dwarf male plant.

The basal cell of a young filament, by which it is fastened to the substratum, is usually modified to form a holdfast, for it is disk-shaped and contains less chlorophyll than the other cells of the filament.

The growth of an *Oedogonium* filament does not take place at its tip, but at various points along its length. The power of division is confined to certain cells which are known as cap cells. These cells periodically divide crossways as long as the filament is growing. Every time such a cell divides the original cell wall splits around its circumference, and the new cell grows out of it, the new cell being formed between the two portions of the original cell. This happens a number of times in the life of a cap cell, and each time it divides a ring is left at one end—hence its name.

The reproduction of *Oedogonium* is also highly specialized. Asexual reproduction is brought about by the formation of zoöspores. Any cell of the filament can produce a zoöspore, its protoplasm separating from the cell and contracting to form a single pear-shaped mass. The pointed end of the spore is colourless and bears a crown of flagella. When the zoöspore is ready for liberation a crack appears at one end of the cell that contains it, and through this split the zoöspore escapes; as the crack is often narrower than the spore, it is necessary for the spore to constrict itself as it passes through. This it appears to do quite easily, without suffering any harm.

On escaping from the filament the zoöspore swims around in the water, often for twenty-four hours or more. Like *Chlamydomonas*, it is sensitive to light, swimming towards moderate illumination, but away from very bright light. With increasing age, however, the zoöspore gradually changes its reaction to light. Its tendency to swim towards moderate light becomes less and less, and finally it avoids light altogether, and so swims downwards into the water. On reaching some solid body it attaches itself by its pointed end, loses its flagella, and secretes for itself a cellulose cell wall, for up to now it has had none. Then it begins to divide, and from it grows out a new filament of *Oedogonium*.

The sexual reproduction of *Oedogonium* is remarkable because, in many species, the male gametes are produced by special very small male plants, known as dwarf males. Species in which this happens are called nannandrous species, from the Latin word *nanus*, a dwarf. First, however, let us look at the simpler type of sexual reproduction found in a macrandrous species, where dwarf males are not formed. In such plants the male reproductive organs, or antheridia, are formed from a cell of the filament which undergoes quickly a number of successive divisions, with the result that a row of short box-like cells is

56

formed. Each of these cells is an antheridium. Each antheridium forms two male gametes which are like smaller and paler editions of the zoöspores, each being pear-shaped, with a crown of flagella at its colourless pointed end.

The female sex organ, or oögonium, is formed from a cell of the filament which swells greatly, taking on an ovoid shape, and accumulates a great deal of cytoplasm, after which its protoplasmic contents separate from the cell wall and form a spherical body, the egg cell. An opening appears in the cell wall near the top of the oögonium, forming a means of entry for the male gamete at the time of fertilization. The male gamete enters through this opening, becomes mingled with the egg cell, the nuclei of the two gametes fusing. The egg cell can now be called an oöspore. This contracts somewhat and secretes around itself a thick cell wall before entering a dormant state. Before dormancy sets in, however, the oöspore loses its chlorophyll and develops a quantity of reddish pigment, and at the same time the cytoplasm produces numerous droplets of oil which will be used as a reserve food material when the oöspore germinates. The oöspore now passes into its resting stage, which may last anything from a few weeks to a few months. When it germinates its thick outer wall is burst by the swelling of the inner layers, and from the contents of the oöspore four zoöspores are formed. These differ from normal zoöspores in having a reddish colour instead of the green of chlorophyll. They are set free in the water, where they swim around for some time, developing chlorophyll as they do so. They then come to rest and germinate in the normal way.

In a nannandrous species of *Oedogonium* the sexual reproduction is rather more complicated. The formation of the oögonium takes place in the way I have already described, but no antheridia are formed. Instead, a row of short cells is produced which somewhat resemble antheridia in appearance, but differ from them in behaviour. Each of these cells produces a single zoöspore, which is smaller than the normal zoöspore, though larger than a male gamete. These special zoöspores are called androspores. They do not germinate like normal zoöspores to produce new filaments, but instead, after swimming about for a short time, they attach themselves to filaments bearing oögonia, usually coming to rest on the wall of the oögonium itself. They germinate to form very small plants, usually consisting of a single basal cell, which serves to attach the dwarf plant to the wall of the oögonium, and a small number of box-like antheridia; sometimes only one antheridium is formed, and in certain cases even the basal cell may be missing. Each antheridium produces two male gametes, each with its crown of flagella. Fertilization then proceeds in the usual way.

The filamentous algae that we have so far considered have all had what are called simple filaments. In some of the more highly developed filamentous algae the filament consists of two parts: a prostrate portion that runs over the surface of the substratum rather like the rhizome of a garden plant such as mint, and several aerial filaments that arise at intervals from the prostrate filament, and which stand more or less erect, supported by the water. This kind of habit is called a heterotrichous filament, and it represents the highest level of development that a filamentous alga can attain. Such a habit may be seen in *Stigeoclonium*, a fairly common fresh-water alga that grows attached to submerged woodwork or stones, or the submerged portions of aquatic plants. The prostrate part of the thallus may be filamentous or flattened, and is branched rather irregularly. From the prostrate portion arise many erect filaments, which are rather sparingly branched. The erect filaments are often covered with a sheath of gelatinous material which is so watery that it is difficult to see under the microscope unless it is treated with suitable stains to make it visible.

Stigeoclonium multiplies quite freely by fragmentation, and it also reproduces asexually by producing zoöspores. These are usually produced in the smaller branches of the erect filaments, each cell producing only one zoöspore, which has four flagella. When specimens of *Stigeoclonium* have been collected and brought back to the laboratory one often finds that zoöspore formation takes place on the following day.

Stigeoclonium also reproduces sexually. The gametes are

formed in a similar way to the zoöspores, but they usually have two flagella instead of four. These biflagellate gametes, when they have been set free in the water, unite in pairs to form a zygote with four flagella, which swims around for a little while and then settles down, loses its flagella, and secretes a cell wall round itself. The zygote may germinate during the next couple of days, but it often undergoes a resting period before germination.

Some species of *Stigeoclonium* have gametes with four flagella. A pair of these, on fusing, will form a zygote with eight flagella. Gametes of this kind are unusual amongst algae.

Cladophora is a very common filamentous alga. Some species of this large genus are marine, while others are found in fresh water. This is unusual among the algae, for most genera are entirely made up of either marine or fresh-water species. *Cladophora rupestris* is a common British species that grows in large quantities on rocks round the coast, usually in the lower part of the littoral zone. It often forms a kind of turf beneath the packed thalli of the serrated wrack, *Fucus serratus*. *C. rupestris* forms small tufted plants up to five inches long, attached to the surface of the rock by short branches called rhizoids. The filaments are dark green and very much branched, so as to present a feathery appearance.

The filaments of *Cladophora* are built up of rectangular cells joined end to end. Each cell contains a single chloroplast, which is in the form of a cylindrical network. The walls of the cells have three layers: an inner one made of cellulose, a middle one containing pectic compounds, and an outer hard layer composed of a material that many authorities believe to be chitin—the hard material that makes up the outer skeletons of insects.

Like *Ulva*, *Cladophora* has an isomorphic alternation of generations. Asexual reproduction takes place by means of zoöspores, which are formed by the young cells near the tips of the branches. The zoöspores have four flagella. They escape from the cells in which they are formed through small circular openings in the cell walls, and it has been observed that, in marine species of *Cladophora*, the escape of the zoöspores usually occurs just as the rising tide washes over the plants. The zoöspores swim around for a time and then settle down and germinate.

The plants that grow from the germinating zoöspores are similar in appearance to the previous ones, but instead of producing zoöspores they produce gametes. These are formed in much the same way as the zoöspores, but they have two flagella instead of four. The gametes fuse together in pairs, producing zygotes which usually germinate within a few days. The germinating zygotes grow into plants that produce zoöspores, and so the cycle goes on.

All the algae that we have so far considered, except *Chlamydomonas*, are divided up into separate cells, either by cross-walls or septa, as in *Spirogyra*, or in the formation of colonies of cells as in *Volvox*. This is not the case with all algae. There is an order called the Siphonales in which there are no septa, the whole structure forming one vast cell in which there are many nuclei. Such a structure is called a coenocyte. It is open to question whether such a structure can be called a cell at all, but we will not trouble ourselves about such points of philosophical nicety.

Bryopsis is a case in point. It is a marine alga, occurring mainly in warm waters, though *B. plumosa* is not at all uncommon round the shores of Britain, and in North America *B. corticulans* is quite common on the Pacific coast. Its habit is different from any alga that we have so far come across. The thallus consists of two parts: a prostrate portion that creeps over the substratum, bearing filaments here and there which stand up vertically, supported by the water; the erect filaments are branched, and the branches bear secondary branches or pinnules. This gives the whole plant, which is usually no more than three or four inches high, a feathery appearance.

Bryopsis plumosa occurs on rocky shores and is sometimes plentiful round the low tide mark, but it is not easily seen, for it loves to hide itself under ledges on the rocks, and also grows on the vertical sides of rock pools where the water is deep. To find it, therefore, you must search for it (Fig. 18).

The inside of *Bryopsis* is continuous from the prostrate system to the topmost pinnule. There are numerous small, disklike chloroplasts and many small nuclei scattered in the cytoplasm that lines the outer wall of the coenocyte, and in the centre is a vacuole containing cell sap. Nowhere is there a cross-septum to interrupt the continuous cavity. Older pinnules, however, may eventually develop septa across their bases, and

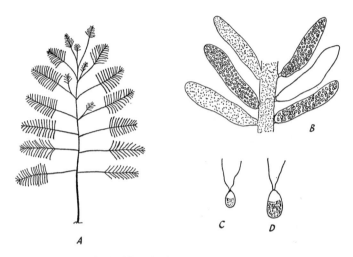

Fig. 18. Bryopsis. A, habit of plant. B, gametangia; on the right a gametangium is empty, having discharged its gametes. C, a male gamete. D, a female gamete.

when they do they drop off. New plants may grow from these shed pinnules.

Reproduction in *Bryopsis* takes place sexually, the pinnules developing into gametangia (structures that contain gametes). Before they do so a cross-wall is formed at the base of the pinna, cutting it off from the rest of the coenocyte. Fruiting takes place mainly in the spring. The contents of the fertile pinna or game-tangium divide up into numerous gametes, of which there are two different kinds. The male gametes are small, with yellowish chloroplasts, while the female gametes are about three times the size of the male and have each a prominent green chloroplast with a pyrenoid. Male and female gametes are formed on different plants, and it is possible to recognize them without microscopical examination, for the male plants have yellowish fertile pinnules while the fertile pinnules of the female plants are dark green.

When the gametes are ready the apex of the pinnule gelatinizes, liberating the gametes into the water. Fusion between a male and a female gamete results in the formation of a zygote which germinates immediately, without first undergoing any resting period.

The coenocytic type of growth may give rise to quite complicated structures, as is seen in *Codium*, a green seaweed that is common in deep pools in the middle of the littoral region of a rocky shore. *Codium tomentosum* has a much-branched thallus which grows attached by a holdfast to the rocks, the individual branches being circular, about the thickness of a lead pencil, and covered with hairs that give it a velvety feeling. When uncovered by the sea it hangs down from the rocks, but when covered by the tide it floats out into the water. It may be up to a foot long. *Codium* forms the favourite food of the sea slug (*Elysia viridis*), and the dark green bodies of the animal are often seen on *Codium* in the south and west coasts of Britain.

The structure of *Codium* is essentially filamentous, but the filaments are woven together to form the large thallus. On the outside the filaments give rise to swollen, elongated vesicles called utricles, which project, rather like a palisade, all round the thallus. The utricles are the organs in which photosynthesis takes place, for most of the chloroplasts are aggregated towards their outer ends, where the light is strongest.

The sexual reproductive organs of *Codium* are formed on the utricles, each utricle usually bearing two gametangia, one on each side. The gametangia are very similar to those of *Bryopsis*. The male gametangia produce a few thousand male gametes which are small, biflagellate, and contain one or two chloroplasts. The female gametangia produce a few hundred female gametes, which are much larger than the male and contain many chloroplasts. Male and female gametes conjugate in pairs, and the resulting zygotes develop immediately into new *Codium* plants.

Codium fragile, growing on the Pacific coast of California, has been seen to discharge its male gametes when the incoming tide floods the thalli. It is by no means unusual for the reproduction of marine algae to be geared to the rhythm of the tides in this way, and in some cases there is even a connexion between the spring or neap tides and the reproductive cycle of the algae.

Meiosis in *Bryopsis* and *Codium*, as far as we know, takes place when the gametes are formed, so that the plants are diploid.

Some members of the Siphonales have a long and prolific fossil history behind them, extending backwards in time for more than 400 million years. These are the Dasycladaceae, one of the best-known fossil groups, whose ancestors go back to Ordovician times, when the land had yet to be populated with plants and the first forerunners of the land flora were still scrabbling in the estuarine mud. The Dasycladaceae reached their greatest development in the Triassic and Jurassic periods and have since declined sadly; of the fifty-five genera that are known, only ten are still living.

The Dasycladaceae owe their long history to the fact that their thalli are liberally encrusted with calcium carbonate, giving them a permanence and a rigidity not usually found among the algae. This habit of wearing an overcoat of lime makes them good material for fossilization, and it is therefore hardly surprising that our fossil records of them go back for a long time. Fossils of the Dasycladaceae have been found in the rocks through most of the geological periods, right back to the Ordovician. Their branched thalli are so characteristic that they can be clearly recognized even in these ancient fossils, although the modern form of the thallus, with its branches arranged in rings, is not seen in rocks earlier than the Triassic.

A charming member of the Dasycladaceae is the mermaid's wine glass, *Acetabularia*. This little plant looks something like a small toadstool, consisting of a slender stalk bearing at its tip a ring of branches which in some species are joined together, forming a cap (Fig. 19). The smallest species grow to a height of something like one-fifth of an inch, but larger species may be as tall as four inches, with caps nearly half an inch wide. *Acetabularia* is usually found in tropical and sub-tropical seas, but it gets as far north as the Mediterranean.

To understand the structure of *Acetabularia* it is best to start with the young thallus growing from a germinating zygote,

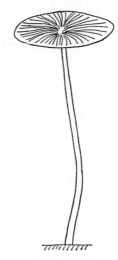

Fig. 19. The mermaid's wine glass (*Acetabularia*).

after sexual reproduction. It grows quickly, one end developing into a system of root-like branches or rhizoids that act as a holdfast while the other grows up vertically. As the vertical part gets longer a ring of fine, hair-like branches is formed at its tip. These are soon shed, each hair leaving a circular scar on the surface of the axis, just as a leaf leaves a leaf-scar behind it when it falls from a tree. Other rings of hairs are formed, one above the other, as the axis grows upwards, and each in turn is shed, leaving behind it a ring of scars.

When the axis has reached its full height it forms at its tip the fertile disk. This consists of a ring of branches which in some species are free from one another, while in others they are joined to form a flat plate. In the middle of the upper face of the disk there is another ring of branches, the ends of which may bear fine hairs, forming what is called the corona superior.

Plate 6. Thallus of *Codium fragile*. On the right can be seen *Fucus serratus* (top) and *F. vesiculosus* (below), while on the left are a few strands of the eel grass (*Zostera*), a marine angiosperm. Bembridge, Isle of Wight

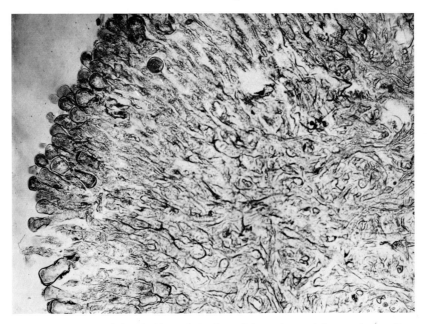

Plate 7. Section of the thallus of *Codium*. Note the utricles at the surface of the thallus

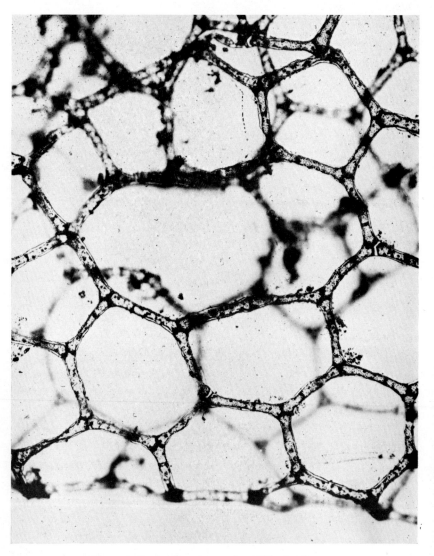

Plate 8. Part of a network of *Hydrodictyon*

In some species of *Acetabularia* there is a similar structure, called the corona inferior, underneath the disk.

The fertile disk contains the gametangia which give rise to the gametes, though their development is a little indirect. The contents of the gametangia divide up into a number of portions called cysts, each of which is protected by a fairly substantial cell wall which, at least in *Acetabularia mediterranea*, is calcified. The cysts are set free in the water and may remain dormant until the following spring. Before they germinate their contents divide up to form a large number of biflagellate gametes which fuse in pairs to form zygotes, from which new *Acetabularia* plants develop.

A strange feature of *Acetabularia* is that for most of its life it has only one nucleus. This remains near the base of the axis and enlarges to about twenty times its original diameter. When the fertile disk is formed the nucleus divides many times, and streaming movements of the cytoplasm carry nuclei to the apex of the axis, where most of them migrate into the gametangia.

Before concluding this account of some of the Chlorophyta I want to return for a moment to some simple one-celled algae that belong to the order Chlorococcales, for these will play a central part in the next chapter. A very well-known example is *Chlorella*. This consists of a single spherical cell, rather like *Chlamydomonas*, but differing from it in having no flagella, and therefore no power of movement. Each cell contains a large chloroplast. *Chlorella* has only one method of reproduction, the cell dividing into from two to sixteen portions called autospores which, when set free by the breaking down of the original cell wall, grow into new individuals of *Chlorella*.

Chlorella is interesting from several points of view. It is one of the algae that have been used in efforts to produce food material that can be supplied to underdeveloped parts of the world. It reproduces very rapidly, and attempts have been made to grow it in bulk in large tanks. I will say more about this in a later chapter. *Chlorella* is also important as one of the algae used by research workers investigating the mechanism of photosynthesis. Some species of *Chlorella* live in association with animals, inhabiting their bodies and setting up a partnership in which the alga supplies its animal host with food materials that it elaborates by photosynthesis, no doubt receiving in return some other substance that it needs. Genera related to *Chlorella* are also found in the lichens, where they are partnered with fungi in one of the most extraordinary and successful co-operative enterprises in the whole living world.

Some of the near relatives of *Chlorella* are colonial. A common one is *Pediastrum*, which forms part of the fresh-water plankton. The colonies are flat and disk-like and may consist of anything up to 128 cells, the exact number varying according to the species (Fig. 20). The cells round the edge of the colony

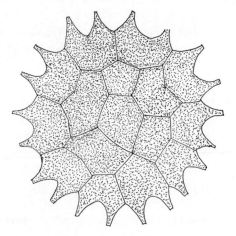

Fig. 20. A colony of *Pediastrum.*

usually have horn-like outgrowths, and some species are also provided with gelatinous bristles. When young each cell has a single nucleus, but as the cells get older the number of nuclei per cell increases, so that when the cells are fully matured each may have as many as eight.

Pediastrum reproduces asexually by producing zoöspores, each of which has two flagella. Zoöspores are generally formed at daybreak. A thin-walled balloon-like vesicle grows out of the parent cell and into this the zoöspores are discharged, but they

66

are not finally liberated until after they have come together and arranged themselves into a new colony.

Pediastrum can also reproduce sexually by forming gametes that are very similar to the zoöspores in appearance. The gametes fuse together in pairs, and the zygotes so formed grow for a time and then divide up to form zoöspores. When these are set free they swim about for a short time and then come to rest, developing into rather irregular polyhedral cells with thick walls. These polyhedra, in turn, produce more zoöspores, which this time are liberated into a vesicle, and these zoöspores join together and form new colonies.

Some of the most beautiful of the colonial algae are the water nets (*Hydrodictyon*), the commonest of which, *H. reticulatum*, is world-wide in its distribution. This has the appearance of a hollow network, oval in outline, and up to eight inches long, that floats majestically in the water. The net is formed from large cylindrical cells.

H. reticulatum reproduces asexually by means of biflagellate zoöspores which, when fully formed, swim about inside their parent cell for a time before they come together and form a new colony, and only then are they set free by the breaking open of the cell in which they were formed. Sexual reproduction also takes place in much the same way as in *Pediastrum*.

Another common colonial member of the fresh-water plankton is *Scenedesmus*, which forms small colonies consisting of four, eight, or occasionally sixteen cells, stuck together in a row (Fig. 21). The cells at the ends of the row often bear horns, and in some species some or all of the cells of the colony are provided with gelatinous bristles. *Scenedesmus*, like *Chlorella*, is a great favourite with plant physiologists for experimental work on photosynthesis.

The Chlorophyta are a very large and interesting group of algae and contain many other important forms, but space forbids us to consider them here. They all share one feature that is very significant in relation to the history of the plant kingdom as a whole, and that is that their photosynthetic pigments are present in their chloroplasts in much the same proportions as they are in the chloroplasts of the higher plants. This, in conjunction with other considerations, makes it seem reasonably certain that it is from the Chlorophyta that the higher plants have sprung. They were the remote ancestors of all the liverworts and mosses, the ferns and their allies, the conifers and the

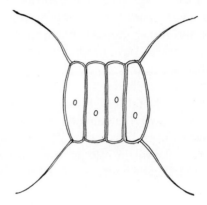

Fig. 21. A colony of *Scenedesmus*.

flowering plants that have so successfully left the water and colonized the land. How that colonization first took place we can only guess, for fossil records are entirely lacking; we only know that it happened a very long time ago. When we look at the Chlorophyta, however, we are looking at the ancestors of our garden plants of today.

CHAPTER 6

Algae in partnership

The algae enter into various partnerships with other plants and animals in which both members of the partnership gain some advantage from the association. Chief amongst these symbioses are the lichens, where an alga and a fungus set up house together for mutual benefit.

Lichens have been known since the time of the ancient Greeks, if not before. It was the Greeks who gave us the word 'lichen', which means 'scaly', an apt description of their dry, greenish-grey thalli. Both Theophrastus and Dioscorides mention their use in medicine and in making dyes; interest in both these uses declined, but has since reawakened. The use of lichens in medicine has lately been revived by the discovery that they are producers of antibiotics, while their use as sources of dyestuffs, which was abandoned with the introduction of synthetic dyes in 1890, has received a new lease of life with the recent boom in home weaving.

At first the algal partner in the lichens was thought to be part of the reproductive structure, and that mistake has been perpetuated in the use today of the term 'gonidia' for the algal cells. The dual nature of the lichens was first recognized by Schwendener in 1867, who thought that the fungi were parasitic on the algae, but later the true nature of the lichen was recognized, and the term 'symbiosis' was applied to them in 1879 by the great mycologist de Bary.

In a lichen most of the thallus is contributed by the fungus, and is constructed from the interwoven threads or hyphae of which the bodies of nearly all fungi are made. Lichens can be divided into two groups according to the distribution of the algal partner or phycobiont within the fungal growth. In most lichens the cells of the phycobiont are arranged in a thin zone beneath the surface of the lichen, and the algae concerned are mainly members of the Chlorophyta such as *Trebouxia* and *Chlorella*. In some lichens, however, the algae are fairly uniformly scattered throughout the thallus, and where this happens the algae are usually members of the Cyanophyta, such as *Gloeocapsa, Nostoc* or *Rivularia*.

The fungal member of the partnership, or mycobiont, is nearly always a member of the great fungal group known as the Ascomycetes, in which the reproductive organs are of a peculiar kind called asci. I will describe the structure of an ascus presently.

The lichens are found growing in a great variety of different places, and often they are to be seen in situations where one would scarcely think that life was possible. *Xanthoria parietina*, for instance, grows on bare rocks near the sea, where it makes great orange splashes of colour. Many lichens grow on tree-trunks and on old roofs, and there are very many of them on the ground, especially on heaths and moors, though they are so inconspicuous that we fail to notice them unless we look.

Lichens show a great variety of form, varying from diffuse lichens that make a thin covering to the substratum on which they are growing, to quite highly organized thalli in which several different zones are apparent. A typical foliose or leafy lichen shows an upper cortex of fungal hyphae which are gelatinized to a greater or less extent, underneath which is an algal zone consisting of the cells of the phycobiont associated with rather loosely arranged fungal hyphae. Below this is the medulla, a thick zone of loosely arranged hyphae, and below this again is the lower cortex in which the hyphae are once more tightly packed. The lower cortex often bears thread-like organs, the rhizinae, which serve to attach the thallus to the substratum.

The fruticose lichens have thalli which either stand erect or else hang down from the surface on which they are growing. They are often branched. The thallus consists of a fairly thick cortex, an algal zone and a central medulla, and they are attached to the substratum by rhizinae which often arise from structures resembling the holdfasts of marine algae. The erect forms may rise to a height of 15 centimetres in a large species, while pendant forms may hang down to a length of as much as 40 centimetres. The well-known reindeer 'moss' (*Cladonia rangiferina*), one of the principal foods of the reindeer in Lapland, is an example of a fruticose lichen.

At the other end of the scale the crustaceous lichens show very little internal differentiation. They form thin growths, usually on rock or the bark of trees, and consist of a thin cortex, a rather diffuse algal zone and a medulla. There is no lower cortex, and the lichen may be partly or completely immersed in the substratum.

Reproduction in the lichens is complicated by the fact that they are dual organisms, and any reproductive system, to be effective, should take into account both the phycobiont and the fungus. It is true that both members of the partnership are capable of an independent life in Nature as well as in the laboratory, and the lichen could, at least theoretically, arise *de novo* from the separately reproducing alga and the fungus, but to what extent this happens, if it happens at all, is a matter of speculation.

Where the phycobiont is a unicellular alga, such as *Chlorella* or *Trebouxia*, it is, of course, reproducing by cell division all the time that the lichen is growing, for it must keep pace with its fungal partner if the dual structure of the thallus is to be maintained. This presents no problem. As the thallus slowly increases in extent the algal cells divide, so that new areas of thallus are populated as fast as they are formed.

Many lichens bear structures that are capable of functioning as vegetative reproductive organs. Isidia, for example, are small outgrowths from the surface of the thallus which contain part of the cortex, algal zone complete with algal cells, and medulla. These can break away and, blown by the wind, create a new lichen thallus elsewhere. Soredia are similar in nature but less highly organized, consisting of small powdery structures generally resulting from the breakdown of the algal layer, and consisting of a small collection of algal cells held together by a weft of fungal hyphae. Like the isidia, they can be carried away by the wind, and where they fall they can germinate to form new lichen thalli.

The fungi which form lichens belong mainly to the Ascomycetes, and as such they have a sexual reproductive process of their own. This is rather complicated and in many cases the details are imperfectly understood, but it results in the formation of structures called asci. An ascus is a usually elongated cell which contains eight spores called ascospores, and the asci are usually massed together in a fruit body of definite shape. In most of the lichen fungi the fruit body is a cup, from 1 millimetre to 2 centimetres in diameter, packed with asci. It is called an apothecium. A few lichen fungi, instead of having an open cup-shaped apothecium, have a hollow flask-shaped structure containing the asci; this is called a perithecium.

Apothecia are of common occurrence on lichen thalli. The ascospores, when they germinate, will give rise to the fungal partner only, for there are no algal cells connected with them. It will therefore be necessary for the lichen thallus to be reconstituted by combination with a suitable algal partner. There is no theoretical reason why this should not happen in Nature, for the lichen-forming algae are extremely common, but the fact remains that the process has never been observed in the field, nor has the complete synthesis of a lichen yet been achieved in the laboratory by adding the correct partner to a culture of the appropriate fungus. This has led some people to the belief that ascospore formation is a purely vestigial process, the fungus 'remembering' what it used to do when growing by itself, and that it plays no part in the reproduction of lichens. Against this extreme view is the undoubted fact that lichens without isidia or soredia produce more apothecia than those in which structures for vegetative reproduction are present, which suggests that the apothecia are not without a reproductive function.

It used to be thought that one particular alga combined with one particular fungus to produce one particular lichen, but recently some doubt has been thrown upon this. *Xanthoria parietina* has been shown to have a different phycobiont in Finland from what it has elsewhere. The question of specificity is a difficult one and is bound up with the existence of different 'strains' of algae which, though identical in form, behave slightly differently in culture. Different strains of algae can be isolated from the same lichen thallus. Much work remains to be done on this question before we can be certain one way or the other.

It is not difficult to isolate the algal partner from a lichen thallus. It can be done under the microscope, using a micropipette to pick up a few algal cells, uncontaminated with fungal hyphae, and transfer them to some sterile culture medium in another dish; or it may be possible to culture a portion of the thallus in a way that slows down the growth of the fungus without interfering with the alga. When separated from their fungi the algae grow in culture quite easily.

The commonest phycobiont in lichens is the alga *Trebouxia*. This is a green alga of the order Chlorococcales, consisting of a single cell with a massive chloroplast, but no flagella or contractile vacuoles. When growing in a liquid medium—and possibly in nature during wet weather—it reproduces by dividing up into motile zoöspores in much the same way as *Chlamydomonas*, but it more commonly forms autospores. These are non-motile spores formed by division of the cell, and there may be from eight to a hundred or more from one cell. When enclosed in a lichen thallus zoöspores are never formed.

When grown in culture *Trebouxia* is a very hardy species, resistant to such things as extremes of temperature and desiccation. Unlike most unicellular algae it can live in very poor light, and when the light is insufficient for photosynthesis it lives as a saprophyte, getting its carbon from organic compounds instead of from carbon dioxide in the air.

Other green algae that are commonly found in lichen thalli include *Chlorella*, *Palmella*, *Protococcus*, and *Trentepohlia*.

Among the blue-green algae that form lichens, *Nostoc* may be taken as an example. This is a common soil alga, having the form of a chain of spherical cells. When it exists in a lichen it may lose its typical chain form and produce instead little clusters of cells.

Studies have been made of substances excreted into the culture medium in which *Nostoc* is growing, and these have been found to include vitamins, polysaccharides, nitrogen compounds of various kinds and even substances that inhibit the growth of the mycobiont. It can be shown that the mycobiont can live purely on these substances, and this raises the interesting question of whether in the lichen the mycobiont is living on substances excreted by the alga, or whether more active means of extraction are employed. A parasitic fungus generally absorbs nutriments from its host by means of little projections, called haustoria, that penetrate the host cells. Does the same thing take place in lichens, or are the algal cells merely in close contact with the fungus without being actually invaded by haustoria?

There is no doubt about the closeness of the association between alga and fungus in a lichen. Commonly the algal cells are not lying free in the algal zone, but are tightly clasped by short branches that are put out by the fungal hyphae. Probably these branches are absorptive, enabling the fungus to savour to the full the substances given out by the phycobiont. In some lichens, however, the fungus goes further than this, for the hyphae have been shown to form haustoria that penetrate into the algal cell. How far this is common in lichens we do not know, for up to date only a few lichens have been closely studied. It may well be that the formation of haustoria by lichen fungi is much more common than we think.

We do not know what it is that the fungus obtains from its partner. Since the algae are photosynthetic it is tempting to suppose that sugar, or some other carbohydrate, makes up the alga's contribution to the partnership, but in Nature the obvious is not always the right solution. It might be nitrogen compounds that the fungus finds it easier to get second-hand, or it might be a vitamin or some other substance that is necessary for its growth.

Many fungi can synthesize all the substances needed for their growth if given suitable organic and inorganic compounds for a starting-point, but others cannot. Many fungi, for instance, need to be supplied with minute quantities of thiamin (vitamin B_1) before they will grow well, and several other vitamins are known to be needed by certain fungi. These vitamins are made by green plants, and it might be the vitamins manufactured by the algae, rather than the sugar, that are the vital factor in the lichen relationship.

With this possible relationship in view, many people have investigated the vitamin requirements of some of the lichen fungi in the hope that they could pin down the nature of the substance or substances that the fungi take from their phyco-bionts. The fungi have been grown in isolation without their algae in media whose precise composition was known, and the effects of adding one or other of the vitamins have been noted. The results were somewhat inconclusive. Some of the fungi appeared to need thiamin in the medium if they were to make adequate growth, but others seemed to be able to fend for themselves without any addition of vitamins. At present the matter must still be regarded as unproved.

If the advantage gained by the fungus from its association with an alga is uncertain, the advantage to the alga is even more problematical. Certainly it gets shelter, and by hiding itself away inside the thallus of a fungus it contrives to live in places where unprotected it would die, but we do not know if this is the whole story. It has been suggested that the alga uses ascorbic acid, produced by the fungus, for respiration, but so far there is no evidence of this.

The isolation of the fungal constituent of a lichen into pure culture is usually not at all difficult. Hyphae may be teased out from the medulla of the lichen, where there are no algae, or ascospores of the fungus may be collected and allowed to ger-minate on a sterile culture medium. When the fungus is isolated it usually grows rather slowly, and does not produce its typical form of thallus, forming instead a rather diffuse weft of hyphae. They do not reproduce in pure culture. Many of them produce coloured pigments, and as this is also characteristic of many

75

lichens it suggests that pigment production may be a property of the fungus and not related to the state of symbiosis that exists when the fungus is accompanied by its appropriate alga.

Attempts have been made to reconstitute a lichen thallus by mixing a pure culture of a lichen fungus with its appropriate alga, but none has been completely successful. Usually the two constituents grow quite independently of one another. Where the medium is low in nutrients, or on substances such as wood in place of agar, the initial stages of synthesis were sometimes observed, and one worker claimed to have produced a structure comparable with a natural lichen thallus. In general, however, lichens appear to be only formed in Nature.

A feature of all lichen thalli is their extremely slow growth—so slow that it is difficult to measure it with any accuracy. Annual measurements are of little value, because in many cases the variation in size of the thallus with its water content at the moment of measuring may be greater than the actual growth in a year. Longer-term observations are apt to fail because of the difficulty of marking the lichen with anything sufficiently durable. Paint has been tried, but is usually found to be inadequate. In temperate climates crustaceous lichens have been found to grow about 0·5 millimetres a year, while non-crustaceous species may grow from 5 to 30 millimetres a year. No lichen has been reliably reported as growing more than 4 centimetres a year. Young thalli grow faster than old, and records exist of lichens which have not grown perceptibly in fifty years.

Although growth is very slow, maturity is reached relatively early, for in most cases fruit bodies are produced within eight years. The life-span of a lichen is probably very great, though we do not know how old they grow. Some crustaceous species are believed to live for 400 years, and in the arctic *Rhizocarpon geographicum* is said to reach an age of 4,500 years, which is about the same life span as that of one of the giant redwood trees of California.

The reason for the very slow growth rate of most lichens is obscure. It has been suggested that the need to secure a balanced growth rate between the fungus and the algal component may have something to do with it, though it is hard to see how that could account for such an abnormally slow growth as is shown by most lichens. Another theory that has been put forward is lack of light. The phycobiont is buried in fungal mycelium, which must to some extent interfere with the light that reaches it for photosynthesis. However, there is no evidence that lack of light is a limiting factor on growth. We shall have to await further knowledge before we can advance a satisfactory reason for the slow growth of lichens.

Since many lichens grow in places, such as outcrops of rocks, where the water supply is at best intermittent, their water relations have aroused the interest of several workers. Lichens usually absorb water over the whole of their thalli, and it is not surprising that the water content of a lichen will vary widely according to whether the surroundings are wet or dry. The amount of water contained in the thallus may be as low as 2 per cent of the dry weight under conditions of extreme desiccation and rise to over 30 per cent when saturated by rain. The rate at which water equilibrium is reached with the environment can be very rapid; some species reach equilibrium in as short a time as one minute, while others may take ninety minutes. Some crustaceous lichens, however, are covered with substances that are water resistant, so that they cannot be wetted. In these cases intake of liquid water would appear to be impossible, and the lichen must rely on taking in water vapour from a humid atmosphere. This will be a slower process, and the lichen may take from one to nine days before it reaches water equilibrium.

Lichens can withstand prolonged periods of drought, though perhaps not so long as they are sometimes credited with. It is very difficult to decide just when a lichen is dead, for most of them look dead anyway. For this reason one must accept with some reserve that a certain lichen from the Libyan desert survived five years of drought, although the algal part of it certainly proved capable of growth when the specimen was brought back to England at the end of the period. In some carefully controlled experimental work it was found that the maximum period that a lichen could withstand without water varied from eight weeks in one species to sixty-two weeks in another. The drought resistance was measured both in an ordinary room and in a desiccator over phosphorus pentoxide, and no difference was observed between the two treatments. This leads to the conclusion that it is the duration rather than the extent of the desiccation that is important. In nature a lichen, even when growing in the driest habitat imaginable, would be unlikely to have to withstand more than forty days without water, remembering that even a fall of dew would break the period of desiccation.

At the other end of the scale, complete submergence of lichen thalli in water for prolonged periods has shown that, in general, species from moist habitats are unharmed, while species from drier habitats may suffer serious damage. This, perhaps, is no more than might be expected.

Lichens, like everything else that is alive, must have food, and it is sometimes a little difficult to see where it comes from. A lichen growing on a bare rock surface, or on the roof of a house, can hardly be expected to draw the nutrients it needs from the substratum beneath it. Many lichens must depend on the atmosphere for their mineral needs, and the idea is not so fantastic as it sounds. Rain water is seldom pure, contrary to popular belief, and where it has splashed from the soil or dropped from rocks overhead it contains a surprising amount of mineral matter in solution. Dust also is universal, and the mineral matter it contains no doubt helps a great deal. It must be remembered that the extremely slow growth rate of lichens does not require a liberal supply of food.

Although the majority of lichens are thus independent of their substratum for food, many of them are quite choosy about what they will grow on. Some will grow on siliceous rocks but not calcareous ones, and many show preferences for certain tree species. Near towns calcareous rocks are in general preferred to siliceous, probably because they tend to neutralize the effect of excessive sulphur dioxide in the air.

The effect of lichens on the rock they grow on has given rise to a certain amount of argument. It used to be thought that they were agents in the erosion of rock, helping to break the rock down into soil, but nowadays this view is frowned upon. It is true that aqueous extracts of lichen thalli are capable of reacting with rock, but whether these substances are actually given off by living lichens is not known. However, lichens probably do help to break up rock by purely physical action when they contract when dry and swell again when wetted, though the total amount of such action is not thought to be very great, at any rate in most cases.

It is a remarkable thing that lichens are some of the most sensitive plants to polluted atmosphere, which is why they are absent from cities and towns, only a few species being found in the outermost suburbs. The deciding factor that limits their growth seems to be the presence of noxious gases in the atmosphere. Which ones are mainly to blame is not certain; sulphur dioxide has been suggested, while the comparative absence of lichens by the sides of main roads has been put down to ozonated hydrocarbons in the exhaust fumes of motor cars, though tar and oil splashed from the road in wet weather might be at least a contributory cause.

There is one lichen, *Lecanora conizaeoides*, which appears to have considerable resistance to pollution, and in the neighbourhood of towns this lichen quickly becomes dominant above all others.

One of the outstanding characteristics of many lichens is the production of a large number of lichen substances, most of which appear to be unique to lichens. These lichen substances are organic compounds of various kinds, and they can in exceptional cases amount to as much as 20 per cent of the dry weight of the lichen, though from 2 to 5 per cent is an average figure. The lichen substances are found for the most part outside the cells, and the reason for their production, sometimes in large quantities, is obscure.

The lichen substances are, in the main, insoluble in water, more or less soluble in alcohol and readily soluble in acetone or chloroform. Most of them are colourless, but a few are brightly coloured; the orange colour of *Xanthoria parietina*, which adds

79

greatly to the gaiety of the scene where it occurs on rocks at the seaside, is due to a lichen substance called parietin.

The occurrence of these bright colours gave the lichens one of their earliest uses—the extraction of dyes that could be used for dyeing fabrics. The species used depended upon the locality. In the Mediterranean *Rocella* was the most popular source of dye, and for many years its distribution was controlled by the Florentine merchants. In Scotland and in Scandinavia species of *Parmelia* were used a lot to provide lasting dyes, and also *Ochrolechia tartarea*, whose dye, though less fast, was useful in combination with certain colours. Lichens provided the colours that dyed Scottish tartans; most of them were derivatives of orcinol which gave beautiful colours when treated with ammonia in the form of stale urine. The introduction of synthetic aniline dyes during the latter part of the last century put paid to the lichen colours as a commercial proposition, but there has lately been a welcome reawakening of interest in connexion with home weaving, and there has recently been a book published on the extraction and use of lichen dyes.

An offshoot of the lichen dye industry was the preparation of litmus, used in the chemical laboratory as an indicator of acidity or alkalinity. This branch of the industry flourished particularly in Holland.

Another ancient use for lichens which has lately been revived is their employment in the preparation of hair and toilet powders, for which they were used extensively during the seventeenth century. Subsequently they went completely out of use, but they have since been revived for modern high-class perfumes. Species of *Evernia*, and sometimes of *Ramalina*, are most popular. They provide oils and derivatives of evernic acid which are used as perfumes, and also for fixing the perfume in scents and soaps.

The most important use for lichens at the present time is undoubtedly for grazing animals, especially reindeer and caribou. Lichens are very indigestible, but certain animals have in their gut bacteria that can break down lichenin, the most important constituent of lichen cell walls. Lichens are of the greatest importance in subarctic regions, where the reindeer

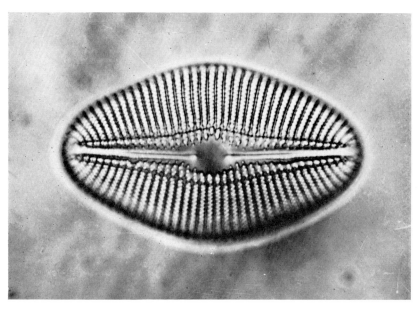

Plate 9. Navicula smithii, a diatom

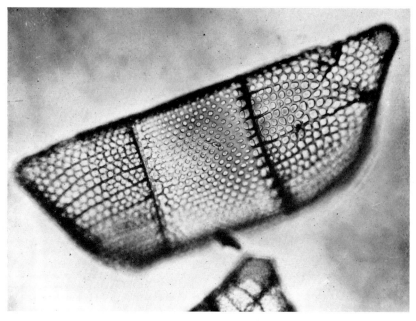

Plate 10. Isthmia nervosa, a diatom

Plate 11. High magnification photograph of part of the frustule of *Pleurosigma formosum*, a diatom, showing the markings

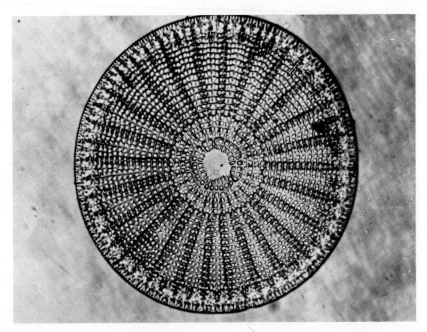

Plate 12. Arachraicliacus ehrenbergi, a centric diatom

'moss' (*Cladonia rangiferina*) and the Iceland 'moss' (*Cetraria islandica*) are present in such quantity on the arctic heaths that reindeer and caribou can graze on them and still leave enough to be harvested for winter food.

Lichens have been used as food by man, but they do not appear to have much to recommend them. The manna of the Bible is usually supposed to have been *Lecanora esculentia*, a lichen that is often blown by the wind in quantity from uplands across deserts. Lichens can be used to make broth and even bread for people whose digestions are upset, though they should be well boiled first in order to destroy substances that might cause inflammation of the intestine.

Letharia vulpina has been used as a poison bait for wolves, but its success in this role is hard to judge, since it was commonly mixed with powdered glass. Any fatalities amongst the wolves were probably due to the powdered glass rather than to the lichen, which by itself would probably not give a wolf anything more lethal than a stomach ache.

In the past lichens have been used to provide a sugary liquid which could be fermented into alcoholic beverages of various kinds. This use died out, but has been revived on a small scale in Russia.

Another ancient use for lichens was for providing medicine, though the value of dosing with lichen is open to doubt. The medical use of lichens has recently been revived by the discovery that many lichens produce antibiotic substances of the same general nature as penicillin. They have been used with success against various skin diseases, and usnic acid, an antibiotic obtained from species of *Usnia*, has been used, in conjunction with streptomycin, in the successful treatment of tuberculosis.

Parmelia furfuracea was sometimes used by the Egyptians as an internal stuffing for mummies. This might be the earliest recorded use of an antibiotic to resist decomposition.

Although it may be seen that the lichens have many uses, it is not very likely that they will ever play a major part in industry, because of their very slow growth rate. One cannot foresee the culture of lichens on a large scale in fermentation tanks for the production of antibiotics, or the setting up of lichen farms in order to provide material for the perfume industry. If someone could find a technique to bump up their growth rate a hundred-fold it would be another matter, but this is in the highest degree unlikely. However, they are very interesting plants, well worth studying for their own sake, and if something useful came out of lichenology it would not be the first time that an unlikely starter has walked away with the race.

The lichens are the biggest group in which algae appear as symbionts, but they are by no means the only one. I have already mentioned the zoochlorellae and zooxanthellae that occur in animal tissues. These are surprisingly common in the animal kingdom, especially among the lower orders.

The commonest instance of a green alga forming zoochlo-rellae in the body of an animal is the green hydra (*Chlorohydra viridissima*), which gets its green colour from the presence in its tissues of minute green cells which have variously been reported to be of the algal genera *Carteria* or *Chlorella*. The algae inhabit the endoderm—the inner layer of the two-layered body wall of the hydra. They reproduce by cell division, and when the *Hydra* reproduces they are passed on to the offspring. There is little doubt of the symbiotic nature of the relationship. Probably the animal benefits from the photosynthetic activity of the algae, which in turn feed on the waste materials, particularly the nitrogenous waste, of the animal, which also benefits from having its nitrogenous excretions used up in this way.

Zoochlorellae and zooxanthellae occur in many Protozoa, such as *Noctiluca*, one of the organisms responsible for the phosphorescence that is often visible in the sea, especially in the tropics. They also occur in the sponges and in many of the jelly-fish phylum (Coelenterata), to which *Hydra* belongs. Zoochlo-rellae are algae mainly belonging to the Chlorococcales, although some of the chlamydomonads, such as *Carteria*, are also found. Zooxanthellae are yellow-green algae; less is known about them, but they appear to belong to the Chrysophyta and possibly the Pyrrophyta.

One of the most extraordinary instances of zoochlorellae is found in the marine worm *Convoluta roscoffensis* which occurs on the coast of Brittany. *Convoluta* is not a segmented worm like the earthworm; it is a turbellarian, belonging to the phylum Platyhelminthes, which also includes the tapeworm and the liver-fluke. It is like a fragment of a delicate leaf, about one-eighth of an inch long by a sixteenth of an inch broad, and coloured deep spinach green by the thousands of tiny green cells that occupy its body. It has a mouth on its under side, and a pair of eyes. It lives in the intertidal zone, near to the high tide mark, where it forms a green belt on the sand. If anyone should approach the *Convoluta* belt incautiously, however, the green colour quickly disappears, for the animals are sensitive to vibrations in the ground and unless one moves with velvet footfalls they quickly bury themselves in the sand.

The green cells of *Convoluta roscoffensis* lie just beneath the surface of the body. So closely integrated are they with the cells of the animal that at first glance their foreign nature would hardly be suspected, but they are, in fact, the cells of a unicellular alga called *Carteria*, a near relative of *Chlamydomonas*. When living independently *Carteria* has four flagella projecting from its front end, but when it adopts a life of symbiosis inside *Convoluta* it loses its flagella and becomes immobile, living in the body cells of the animal as if it were a part of them. The appearance under the low power of the microscope is as if the cells of *Convoluta* contained chloroplasts, like plant cells.

Convoluta roscoffensis shows a plant-like characteristic in that it is attracted by light or, as we say, positively phototactic. If individuals are placed in a shallow dish, and one end of the dish is illuminated while the other is kept in darkness, *Convoluta* will make its way towards the light end and stay there. This behaviour ensures that the green cells will have light for their photosynthesis, and is a clear indication, if one is needed, that *Convoluta* benefits from the photosynthetic activities of its partner. Its habit on the beach is similarly motivated. *Convoluta* occupies a restricted zone on the foreshore just below the high tide mark for neap tides. Higher than this it cannot go, for it would then be left high and dry and would soon perish. On the other hand, if it ventured too far towards the sea it would be forced below the surface of the sand by wave action for most of the time and would therefore be unable to make the most of what light is available. *C. rostochensis* is a delicate creature and is quite unable to withstand the pounding of the waves as the tide advances; when the tide gets near it is warned by the vibration of the ground, caused by the waves, that it is time to seek safety, and it promptly sinks into the sand until the tide goes out again.

If an adult *Convoluta roscoffensis* is captured and examined, a strange thing appears. Although it is an animal, no trace of food material can be found in its body. Even if it is kept in filtered sea water for a fortnight, by which time it should be ravenous, and then tempted with morsels of food like diatoms, green algae, oil drops or milk, it not only refuses them, but keeps its mouth pursed up so as to be invisible. This is strange behaviour for marine turbellarians, which are notoriously hungry for most of the time. The answer is that *C. roscoffensis* is kept supplied with food by its algal partner and so does not need to eat. The alga is making sugar all the time by photosynthesis and some of this sugar goes to feed its host, which in time becomes totally dependent on its partner.

When a young *Convoluta* is first hatched from the egg it contains no green cells, but it soon develops them, being 'infected' with algal cells from the sea water in which it lives. During this early period *Convoluta* feeds exactly like any other animal, taking in diatoms and other marine bric-à-brac through its mouth and digesting them. Then, as the green cells begin to multiply throughout its body, *Convoluta* begins to rely more and more on feeding like a plant. Finally it becomes entirely plant-like in its nutrition.

There is, however, yet another stage in the nutrition of *Convoluta roscoffensis*. When it finally begins to age it turns against the algal cells that have fed it so well and begins to digest them, those at the tail end of the animal usually being digested first.

At this stage one may find individuals with a piebald look; white tails joined to a green head. Gradually the digestion proceeds until there are no green cells left. This is the end of the road for *Convoluta*; reproduction takes place and, with the laying of fertile eggs, the animal dies.

If the association between *Convoluta roscoffensis* and *Carteria* is a true symbiosis, and not a case of simple parasitism by the animal on the plant, the alga must gain something from the association. We are not sure what the plant gains in this case, but it seems reasonable to suppose that nitrogen excreted by the animal is used by the plant in return for sugar that the animal takes from the plant. The possibility of a more complex relationship, however, must always be borne in mind.

Convoluta roscoffensis is an example of an organism where the symbiotic association is obligate, but in some cases it is optional. *Noctiluca*, for instance, is colourless in the North Atlantic but green in the Indian Ocean. Association between animal and plant cells is commoner in the tropics than it is in colder regions. An interesting case is seen in certain reef corals, which have algal cells living in their tissues, but gain no nutritive value from them; nor does the oxygen given off by the algae in photosynthesis bear any relation to the needs of the coral. It is, however, possible that the algae are of service in removing nitrogenous excreta from the cells they inhabit.

There are many records of algal cells living in association with other plants, and even other algae. *Gloeochaete* is now known to be a colourless member of the Tetrasporales, a group of the Chlorophyta, in which the 'chloroplasts' are really a symbiotic blue-green alga. A similar case is seen in *Glaucocystis*, which is a colourless genus in the Chlorococciales, again with blue-green algae inhabiting its cells.

The cycads are a strange group of seed plants to which the term 'living fossil' has been applied on account of their relatively primitive structure. On cycad roots there are short lateral branches which are apogeotropic—that is, they grow in any direction instead of being attracted downwards by the pull of gravity. These apogeotropic roots regularly become 'infected' with the blue-green alga *Anabaena*, which sets up an algal zone in the root. Whether the relationship is symbiotic, or whether it is a simple case of 'space parasitism', is not known with certainty, though the regular occurrence of the algae in the roots of cycads suggests the former.

CHAPTER 7

Plant or animal?

Most people think they know the difference between a plant and an animal. It is so obvious. Nobody in his right senses would think a cabbage was an animal or a kitten was a plant. The difference is one of the things that is instilled into us from childhood, and from an early age it becomes part of our mental make-up. But it is not really so easy as that, and when we come to study biology, and especially the biology of simple organisms like some of the algae, we have to start thinking again.

We all know that an animal can roam around looking for food and anything else it wants, while a plant must remain rooted in one spot for the whole of its life—unless it happens to be one of John Wyndham's tryffids, which, happily, have no place in real life. A moment's thought, however, tells us that this difference is by no means universal. What about the sea anemone? This is an animal, yet it spends most of its life anchored to a rock (it swims around when *very* young, but few people outside a marine laboratory have seen the planula larva of the sea anemone). Many other marine animals are, like the sea anemone, sedentary, spending their adult lives in one place and letting the world go by.

Perhaps you will say that the sea anemone has tentacles that it can wave in the air, thereby showing its animal nature beyond dispute? Permit me to show you a sensitive plant (*Mimosa pudica*). It looks like a perfectly normal plant, but give it a sharp tap across one of its branches and the whole plant folds its leaves, seeming to cower away from such rough treatment. Give it a little while to rest and it opens out and is ready to play again. If you say that this is an exceptional case, just look at any potted plant kept in a room near a window and see how it bends towards the light. The fact is, the power of movement is no means at all of distinguishing a plant from an animal.

Can we find a better criterion? I think we can. Nearly all plants (except the fungi) have chlorophyll and are able to build up their own organic food from simple inorganic compounds. We say that they are holophytic. Animals, on the other hand, have to be supplied with organic food from outside: they are holozoic.

This is a better test for deciding whether an organism is a plant or an animal, but even this is not infallible. Besides the fungi, there are a few higher plants which have no chlorophyll and so must be supplied with organic food: the toothwort is one of them and the bird's-nest orchid another. More difficult still, however, are certain unicellular organisms, of which we have already met one in *Chlamydomonas*. Here the distinction between an animal and a plant really does seem to break down, and you will find these creatures described in textbooks of both botany and zoology. These little organisms used to be known as the Protista—organisms on the borderline between the plants and the animals, of which nobody could say whether they were definitely one or the other.

There is nothing irrational in such a situation. It is a result of the fact that all forms of life have evolved from some primeval living matter that originated, we know not how, a thousand million years or so ago. From this common stock the animal and plant kingdoms diverged from one another; it is hardly surprising that some organisms should remain betwixt and between.

Such a creature is *Euglena*, a member of the Euglenophyta. *Euglena viridis* is often found in puddles, where it may be present in such quantities as to give the whole puddle a green colour. It is an inhabitant of ponds, ditches and stagnant water generally, and is not at all uncommon.

Euglena is a minute, spindle-shaped creature which may reach a length of one-sixth of an inch. It consists of a single cell;

the front end is blunt, while the hinder end is somewhat pointed (Fig. 22). At the front end there is a funnel-shaped ingrowth known as the 'gullet', though there is considerable doubt whether it is ever used for the intake of food, at least in *E. viridis*. The gullet leads into a more or less circular space called the

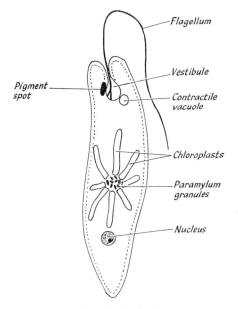

Fig. 22. Euglena.

reservoir, from the wall of which a single flagellum arises and passes out through the gullet. The base of the flagellum appears to be split into two, and bears a swelling which, as we shall see, is sensitive to light.

There is a strong pellicle or 'skin' surrounding the cell of *Euglena*, which helps to maintain its shape. *Euglena* is capable of making wriggling movements—the so-called 'metabolic' movements—but its main source of motility comes from its flagellum. This projects obliquely backwards from the organism, and by its movement propels the little plant-animal forwards with a spirally rolling motion, rather like a drunken porpoise.

The direction of movement of *Euglena* seems to be largely

89

controlled by light. There is a pigment spot or stigma to one side of the reservoir which is composed of numerous red granules embedded in a colourless, concavo-convex matrix. If, in the course of its spiral movement, the stigma throws a shadow on the swelling at the base of the flagellum, the movement is immediately altered until the swelling is no longer in the shade. The importance of the stigma is shown by the fact that those members of the Euglenophyta that have no stigma do not respond to light, although the stigma itself does not appear to be light-sensitive.

On one side of the reservoir is a large contractile vacuole, which discharges into the reservoir. Just before the contractile vacuole collapses a number of small vacuoles appear around it, and after the collapse of the old vacuole these grow and finally coalesce to form the new one. This is a process similar to what happens in many other one-celled organisms, and there is no justification for the story, sometimes told, that the contractile vacuole in *Euglena* is specially complicated.

The cell of *Euglena* contains a nucleus and a number of green, strap-shaped chloroplasts which radiate from a point in the cytoplasm, in front of the nucleus, where granules of a starch-like substance called paramylum collect. Starch is never formed in the Euglenophyta, and paramylum, which is a carbohydrate of somewhat similar composition, takes its place. It forms bodies of various shapes, including disks, rods and rings, which have a high degree of permanence and are used in the identification of species.

Since *Euglena viridis* contains chlorophyll it is able to carry out photosynthesis during daylight. It is very doubtful, however, if it can feed itself entirely in a plant-like manner, though the nearly related *E. gracilis* certainly can. Although *E. viridis* is independent of any source of carbon save carbon dioxide, it still depends on an organic supply of nitrogen; it cannot elaborate the nitrogen compounds it needs from an inorganic source of nitrogen such as nitrates or salts of ammonia. To this extent, therefore, it behaves like an animal.

Euglena reproduces by cell division, which begins at the front

90

end and works backwards. Sometimes cell division may take place in a cyst, in which case it may be repeated several times before the young cells are set free by the breakdown of the cyst wall.

If some species of *Euglena* are kept in the dark the chloroplasts, having no work to do, lose their green colour and finally disappear. The organism does not necessarily die when this happens, however, for, bereft of photosynthesis, it nourishes itself by absorbing organic matter from the water. When a plant does this sort of thing it is said to be saprophytic, while an animal in the same circumstances is saprozoic. Whether *Euglena* reduced to this condition is saprophytic or saprozoic depends on whether you look on it as a plant or an animal.

There are many relatives of *Euglena* which never develop chlorophyll. *Peronema* is such a one, common in stagnant water. It is colourless, and it uses its gullet for taking in the small organisms on which it feeds. Nutrition here is entirely animal, and one would have no hesitation in placing *Peronema* in the animal kingdom.

Several species of *Euglena* contain little red granules of a pigment often referred to as haematochrome. There are probably several of these pigments. The red species of *Euglena* are particularly common in pools which are rich in organic matter, and they grow best at high temperatures. Under the right conditions they may form a dark red scum on the surface of the water, which turns green when the sun disappears behind clouds. This is due to movement of the red granules. In bright light, and particularly at temperatures over 30°C, the granules are evenly dispersed throughout the cell, making it appear red; but in a weaker light and at a lower temperature the red granules aggregate together in the centre of the cell. The chloroplasts, which are arranged round the circumference, are now unmasked, so the organism appears green.

The Euglenophyta are found chiefly in small fresh-water pools that are rich in organic matter, but many occur in brackish and salt water. *Euglena mutabilis* is common in coal-mine pits and grows best in water that is acid. Some live in a variety of animals, including flatworms, earthworms, copepods, rotifers (wheel animalcules), eelworms and amphibians. A few, such as the marine *Colacium arbuscula*, are colonial. The individuals of *C. arbuscula* are without flagella and attached by their hinder ends to branched mucilage stalks; they are usually found attached to organisms of the marine plankton, especially copepods.

CHAPTER 8
The diatoms

The order Chrysophyta contains three distinct classes of algae: the yellow-green algae or Xanthophyceae, the golden-brown algae or Chrysophyceae and the diatoms or Bacillariophyceae. The first two classes contain many interesting and beautiful forms, all of them microscopic, but I do not propose to discuss them here. The diatoms, however, apart from their importance as a major part of the floating life of the sea, have achieved fame in another direction. Every amateur microscopist has at some time or another looked at specimens of diatoms and been entranced by the beauty of the delicate markings on their shells. These markings are of extreme fineness, going up to and even beyond the resolving power of the microscope, and ever since the microscope became popular in Victorian days diatom test slides have been used for checking the performance of microscopical objectives. They are still so used today.

The diatoms are remarkable in a number of ways, for besides the markings on their shells or frustules, to use the correct scientific term, they have a peculiar process called auxospore formation to offset their natural tendency to get smaller and smaller each time they reproduce. Many of them also have a mysterious kind of motility that has never properly been elucidated.

A diatom enclosed in its frustule is like a box with overlapping sides, the top half fitting over the bottom half. The top half is called the epitheca and the bottom half the hypotheca, and both halves are hardened with silica, the material of which sand grains are composed. The parts that correspond with the top and the bottom of the box are called the valves, while the sides of the box are known as the connecting bands. The two connecting bands, which overlap one another, constitute the girdle. One may therefore have two views of a diatom under the microscope: the valve view when one is looking at the top or bottom of the box, and the girdle view when one sees it from the side.

The two valves are ornamented with a complex pattern of dots, but the girdle is plain. The two valves and the girdle are firmly cemented together, and in order to separate them it may be necessary to boil the frustule in concentrated nitric acid.

We can divide the diatoms into two groups, the Centrales and the Pennales, according to the shape of the valves. In the Centrales the valves are usually circular, though they may be triangular or even elliptical, and the markings are radially disposed about some central point. In the Pennales the valves are elliptical or oblong, often many times longer than broad, and the markings are in two series of rows, one on either side of a line running down the middle.

When seen in girdle view the difference between the Centrales and the Pennales disappears, for all, or nearly all, diatoms in girdle view are oblong.

In most of the pennate diatoms there is a groove called the raphe running longitudinally along the centre of the valve, between the two series of rows of dots. This, as we shall see in a moment, is thought to have something to do with the motility of diatoms. In the middle of the valve the cell membrane is thickened to form the central nodule, and here the raphe dips inwards, running in a canal under the nodule and emerging on the other side. At either end of the cell there is a polar nodule within which the raphe ends.

Many Pennales have a raphe on both valves, but some do not. When there is a raphe on one valve only it is always on the valve which is next to the substratum. In the Centrales there is no raphe.

It appears that the raphe contains cytoplasm, continuous with the cytoplasm of the cell. The cytoplasm of the raphe is in a constant state of streaming motion, and it is the friction of the cytoplasmic stream on the surrounding medium that gives the diatoms their peculiar gliding motion. The movement of diatoms is, however, improperly understood.

The markings on diatom frustules have always excited the interest of microscopists, and indeed of anyone who has looked at diatoms through a microscope. Under low or medium powers of the microscope the markings on the frustules of pennate diatoms appear as fine lines, if they are visible at all, but on examination through a high-powered objective they can be resolved into lines of fine dots. With careful focusing they can be made to appear as light dots on a dark background or *vice versa*. Sometimes the dots are so relatively coarse that even a 4-millimetre objective will resolve them, but in others they need the full power of a 2-millimetre oil-immersion objective before they can be seen. *Pleurosigma angulatum* is a case in point. Under the 4-millimetre objective the lines of dots can just be seen, but only as lines. One has no idea of their true structure until one employs the 2-millimetre oil-immersion, when they can readily be seen to consist of separate dots, placed close together. The frustule of this diatom is bent, so that while one part of it is in 'white dot' focus the adjoining part will be in 'black dot' focus.

Even more difficult are *Amphipheura pellucida* and *Suriella gemma*; indeed, the latter will refuse resolution even with a 2-millimetre objective unless it is mounted in something of high refractive index, such as Styrax or realgar.

Diatoms are easily come by and the preparation of diatom slides for the microscope is by no means difficult, though a little patience is needed. Diatoms can be collected from a lake or pond, where they often form slimy masses on the surface of the water, especially in spring and autumn. Many diatoms occur on lake bottoms, and they are common in salt marshes. They may also be scraped off the surface of a stone or a piece of wood that has been immersed for some time in water.

The first thing to do when making a preparation is to separate the diatoms from the mud and debris that are always collected with them, and for this a couple of conical beakers or large wine-glasses are useful. The material containing the diatoms is put into a beaker, shaken up well with water, and allowed to stand for a time. When a considerable amount of the debris has settled the cloudy water containing the diatoms is poured into the other beaker and the process is repeated. This is done several times, until examination of a drop of the fluid under the microscope shows that it contains nothing but diatoms.

Before mounting it may be necessary to concentrate the diatoms in the water by allowing them to stand for a while and then decanting off some of the clear liquid.

A shell mount can now be made. A drop of the water containing the diatoms is put on a cover glass and allowed to dry up in a warm place, protecting it from dust; the water gradually evaporates and leaves the diatoms stuck to the cover glass. We have then to burn away the organic matter, so as to leave only the frustule, and for this the best tool is a strip of copper, about one and a half inches wide and several inches long, mounted in a handle. The cover glass is placed, diatoms upwards, on the copper strip and heated in the flame of a bunsen burner or spirit lamp to burn off the organic matter; care must be taken, of course, to avoid heating to redness, as this would cause the cover glass to warp. Heating is continued until the diatoms turn first brown and then greyish-white, after which they are examined under the low power of the microscope to see whether all the organic matter has gone. If this is so, the diatoms are ready for mounting.

The Canada balsam that is used by microscopists for making permanent preparations of most objects is not good for diatoms. Its refractive index is too near to that of the diatoms themselves, so that the dots do not show up to their best advantage. It is best to use a mountant with as high a refractive index as possible, for the visibility of the dots will be, to some extent, a function of the difference between the refractive index of the mounting medium and the diatom. Realgar, a sulphide of arsenic, is a very good medium, but it is difficult and even dangerous to use on account of its poisonous properties. It is better to use one of the special diatom mounting media, such as Styrax. A drop of

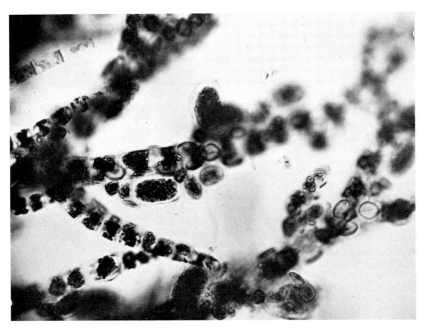

Plate 13. Part of a filament of *Ectocarpus*, bearing unilocular sporangia

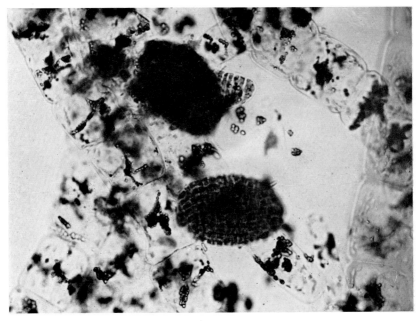

Plate 14. Part of a filament of *Ectocarpus*, bearing plurilocular sporangia

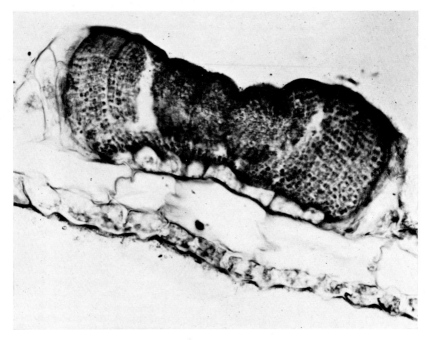

Plate 15. Antheridia of *Dictyota*

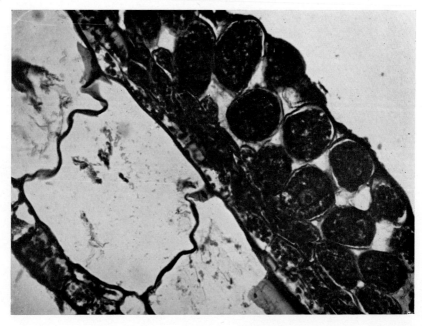

Plate 16. Oögonia of *Dictyota*

Styrax is put on a slide and the cover glass is lowered gently on to it, the diatoms, of course, being placed downwards. When the Styrax has set a completely permanent mount will result. The old microscopists used to arrange diatom frustules in various patterns on their slides. This needs patience, but it is not so difficult as it sounds. For moving the diatoms an eyelash mounted in a wooden handle—or, better still, a bristle from a nylon tooth brush—may be used, the diatoms being kept under observation with the low power of the microscope while they are being handled. With a little practice a surprising amount of dexterity can be attained.

The frustule is, of course, only the outer covering of the diatom. The living part is inside. The cytoplasm lines the frustule, leaving a large vacuole in the centre of the cell. In many Pennales there is a bridge of cytoplasm running transversely across the centre of the cell, dividing the vacuole into two portions, and the nucleus commonly occupies a position in this bridge; in the Centrales it usually lies in the cytoplasm on one side of the cell.

In the cytoplasm are chloroplasts, which vary very much in form. In some Pennales, especially raphe-bearing species, there may be one or two large chloroplasts which lie apposed to the girdle, while in others the chloroplasts may be small and numerous. In the Centrales the chloroplasts may be large lobed disks, but in many of the marine forms they are small and granule-like.

The green colour of the chlorophyll in the chloroplasts is more or less masked by the presence of other pigments, so that the chloroplasts vary in colour from yellow to olive-green or brown. The colour varies with the intensity of illumination. The accessory pigments are much the same as in the brown seaweeds, the principal ones being, besides chlorophyll *a* and *c*, beta-carotene (reddish) and several xanthophylls (yellow).

Diatoms are very widespread in nature, for they are not only abundant in both fresh and salt water, but also occur in the soil in considerable numbers. Many of the raphe-bearing species inhabit the mud or rock both in fresh water and in the sea.

SA–G   97

Diatoms without a raphe are especially abundant in the freshwater plankton, while the marine plankton contains many Centrales. They are often most abundant in the spring. The frustules survive the death of the cells and may give rise to deposits known as diatomaceous earth or kieselguhr. Some very extensive deposits of this nature have been formed in the past, mainly from marine diatoms, though as fossils they are not known from rocks earlier than the Mesozoic. In the Santa Maria oilfield, California, there is a subterranean deposit of diatomaceous earth 3,000 feet thick.

Many diatoms form colonies, the individuals being stuck together by mucilage which is often secreted through large pores on the valves. Some of these colonies may be large and may even be mistaken, at a glance, for brown algae.

Diatoms usually reproduce by cell division, each of the resulting daughter cells adopting one theca of the parent, the other being formed *de novo*. Before the nucleus divides the two thecae of an individual about to divide come apart slightly, though they do not separate entirely. The cell divides along a plane parallel to the valves, the division beginning on the outside and proceeding inwards, the nucleus dividing at the same time. When fission is complete each daughter cell secretes a new valve on the freshly formed surface of its protoplasm, after which a new connecting band is also formed, inside the one that is already there. Thus the connecting band of the parent theca overlaps the new connecting band in each case, and the hypotheca of the old cell becomes the epitheca of one of the new ones.

From this it will be seen that, while one of the new cells is as big as the parent, the other is slightly smaller. Owing to the rigid nature of the silicified wall of the new cell, growth of the cell is precluded, so that this diminution in size is permanent. It therefore follows that the average size of a diatom population must gradually decrease as the population gets older, and this decrease has indeed been followed both in nature and by observations of diatoms kept in culture. The decrease in size is very slow, but spread over several years it becomes very appreciable and constitutes a potential danger to the species. Diatoms do not fade right away, however, for sooner or later the size is restored to its original figure by the process of auxospore formation.

Auxospore formation in diatoms is rather a complex process, and varies somewhat in different species. In the Pennales it usually results from a sexual process of conjugation, in which two individuals lie opposite to one another, often enclosed in a mass of mucilage. In each individual the nucleus divides twice, the divisions being meiotic. Diatoms in their normal state are therefore diploid. After the meiotic division of the nucleus the protoplasm divides into two halves, each containing two haploid nuclei, one of which promptly degenerates. The four half-protoplasts, each now with one nucleus, are then set free by the two parent individuals. These are gametes, and they fuse in opposite pairs, a gamete from one individual fusing with one from the other. Two zygotes are thus formed, and these lengthen to form two auxospores. Within the protective membrane of the auxospore a new diatom is formed, its size being equal to the maximum size for the species.

There are many variations in auxospore formation in the Pennales. In the Centrales the process is different in that it concerns one individual only, there being no process of conjugation preceding it.

In many members of the Centrales the life history is complicated by the formation of microspores. These are minute bodies formed by successive divisions of the parent cell. The microspores are finally liberated into the water, and in some species they may be flagellated. Their subsequent development is in most cases not known, but in one instance, at least, they appear to be male gametes which fertilize a cell containing a single egg. It seems possible, therefore, that the microspores really represent part of the sexual process of the Centrales.

CHAPTER 9
Some more plant-animals

We come once more to a group of organisms that are on the borderline between the plant and animal kingdoms. These are the Pyrrophyta, with only one class, the Dinophyceae or, as the zoologists prefer to call them, the Dinoflagellata. There are more than a thousand species of these unicellular organisms, and they are found in fresh and sea water, in the sand on beaches, and in snow; they also occur as parasites in a variety of animals, including fish, copepods and other invertebrates, and as symbionts in some Protozoa and Coelenterata. Their greatest importance is in the marine plankton, where they exist in countless millions; they are, in fact, second only to the diatoms as producers of organic matter in the sea.

Many marine Dinophyceae are luminescent, causing water that is disturbed to glow with an unearthly phosphorescence at night. This faculty is sometimes used by fishermen, as, for instance, in locating schools of the California sardine or pilchard at night. On the other hand, they are mainly responsible for the occurrence of 'red water', which may be a danger to marine life. The principal causers of red water off the coast of California are *Gonyaulax polyedra* and *Prorocentrum micans*, but various species of *Cochlodinium*, *Gymnodinium*, *Heterocapso* and *Glenodinium* may cause a similar phenomenon elsewhere. *Gonyaulax catenella* has been known to make shellfish poisonous to man during the warmer part of the year on the coasts of California and Oregon, the California mussel being especially liable to be affected.

The Dinophyceae mostly have a very characteristic structure
100

which is readily recognized under the microscope. They are unicellular, varying in shape from nearly spherical to needle-shaped, and they often have horns either before or behind them, or both. The striking feature of most of the Dinophyceae, however, is the way the two flagella lie in grooves on the surface of the cell (Fig. 23). There are two of these grooves. One, known as

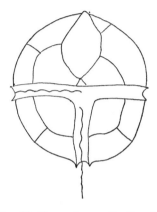

Fig. 23. Gonyaulax, a dinoflagellate.

the sulcus, runs fore and aft, and the longitudinal flagellum, which lies in this groove, projects behind the organism and, by its movement, pushes it through the water. The other groove, which is called the girdle, is transverse, and the flagellum that it houses gives the cell a rotating movement, and may contribute to the forward movement as well.

The cell may reach a high level of complexity, and varies a great deal in different species as regards the details of its structure. The range of colour is enormous, though yellow-brown and yellow-green are the commonest, and the pigments may appear in the chloroplasts, in the form of small granules in the cytoplasm, or just dissolved in the cytoplasm. Chlorophyll *a* and *c* are present, and in addition there are a number of xanthophylls, some of which are only found in the Dinophyceae, and beta-carotene. On the whole the pigmentation resembles that of the diatoms and the brown seaweeds.

101

Chloroplasts are not always present, for there are many species of Dinophyceae that are animal-like in their nutrition. When present, the chloroplasts may be disk-shaped, rod-shaped or star-shaped. The excess carbohydrate is stored up in the form of starch in most fresh-water species, but marine species accumulate oil, and droplets of oil of a bright yellow or red colour are commonly seen in the cytoplasm.

Most Dinophyceae contain curious vacuoles known as pusules. They are large vacuoles which lie near the centre of the cell, with two canals that open to the outside world near to the places where the flagella are inserted. There are commonly two pusules to a cell. Pusules are common in marine Dinophyceae, but rather rare in fresh-water species. They change somewhat in size from time to time but they do not pulsate in the way that contractile vacuoles do. It has been suggested that they may have something to do with the nutrition of the organism, and especially the intake of fluids, but we do not really know what they are for.

Some Dinophyceae are naked, but most are enclosed in a heavy shell made of cellulose, called the theca. When examined under the high power of the microscope the theca appears to be perforated by a large number of very fine holes; this appearance is rather deceptive, and appears to be an optical effect, the 'perforations' being really shallow depressions in the theca. In some species the theca has an elaborate structure, and may be extended into spines or even sails. In some cases these thecal expansions may serve to give the organism extra buoyancy in the water, but in *Citharistes* they form a home for zooxanthellae.

The nucleus of the Dinophyceae is large and the chromatin is arranged rather like a string of beads, an arrangement known as moniliform.

The Dinophyceae reproduce mainly by cell division, and in those species with a well-developed theca the two halves of the shell may be shared between the two daughter cells, each growing a new half-theca. Since the parts of the theca do not fit one inside the other, as in the diatoms, there is no reduction in size following cell division. In some forms, however, the theca breaks

102

open and the living cell emerges before dividing, so that each daughter cell has to grow a complete new theca. Some Dinophyceae form zoöspores.

Sexual reproduction is almost unknown among the Dinophyceae, but a pairing of individuals has been described for *Ceratium* which may be a process of sexual conjugation, and *Glenodinium* is said to reproduce by the mating of motile gametes. Although most of the Dinophyceae are motile and unicellular, some forms exist which are neither. In the order Dinotrichales the individual cells are without flagella and are therefore immobile, and the more or less cylindrical cells are joined together to form branching filaments which grow by cell division. An example is *Dinoclonium conradi*. These filamentous forms reproduce by the contents of a cell dividing up into zoöspores. One would hardly take these filamentous forms for Dinophyceae were it not for the zoöspores, which have the typical dinophycean structure.

In the Dinococcales we also have non-motile forms which have lost their flagella. They have rounded cells—hence their name—and are mainly found in fresh water. Some of them are sedentary, growing attached to other plants by means of a stalk, as in *Stylodinium globosum*; others are parasitic on or in animals. They reproduce by forming zoöspores, and again the zoöspores, by their typically dinophycean appearance, are a clue to the systematic position of the adults.

CHAPTER 10

The brown seaweeds

The brown seaweeds or Phaeophyta are the most familiar of the algae, for anyone who has ever visited the seaside must have trodden over the masses of wrack that cover the rocks and litter the beaches. They are also by far the largest, though they also contain some small members; there are, however, no unicellular brown algae so far known, and no colonial forms. There are three fresh-water genera, the remainder being marine. They grow in their greatest profusion in the zone between the tide marks and in the upper sublittoral zone—i.e. just below low tide mark, where species of *Laminaria* and its allies in particular may form submarine forests. They reach their best development in colder waters, though they are also well represented in the tropics.

The brown algae owe their characteristic olive-green to dark brown colour to the pigment fucoxanthin, which is carried in their chloroplasts. This masks the colour of the other pigments, which include chlorophyll *a*, chlorophyll *c*, several xanthophylls and beta-carotene. It should be remembered that all brown algae are not Phaeophyceae, however, for the thalli of various other algae, and especially the red seaweeds, may be brown as well, superficially resembling the brown algae.

The size of the brown algae is variable. On the one hand, some species of *Ectocarpus* are microscopic, while on the other, the giant kelp *Macrocystis* may have fronds 600 feet long. The complexity of the thallus also varies; the simpler forms are branched filaments, while at the other end of the scale members of the Laminariales and Fucales possess thalli which easily surpass all

104

other algae both in external and internal intricacy of structure.

The cell walls of the brown algae are of two layers, the inner one being composed of cellulose while the other one is of pectic compounds. In most species the chief component of the outer wall is a gum-like substance called algin which is economically valuable for a number of purposes. The cells usually contain many small vacuoles rather than a single large one, and round the nucleus there are a number of vesicles, called fucosan vesicles, containing a substance known as fucosan, which seems to be of a similar nature to tannin. We are not sure what the fucosan is for, but it is probably a by-product of the activities of the cell. The chief storage carbohydrate is a polysaccharide called laminarin, but an alcohol called mannitol also frequently occurs, and oil is also common.

Most brown algae show an obvious alternation of generations, though the Fucales are an exception. In some the sexual and asexual generations are similar and the alternation is therefore isomorphic, but in the Laminariales they are very different from one another, so that the alternation is heteromorphic.

There are altogether about 240 genera in this large group of algae, with about 1,500 species.

As an example of one of the simplest of the brown algae we will consider *Ectocarpus*, which is world-wide in distribution and contains many species. It is often epiphytic; that is, it grows on other plants, especially the large brown seaweeds such as *Fucus* and *Laminaria*. It is very common on British coasts and along the Atlantic coast of the United States, various species growing abundantly on various Fucaceae in the upper littoral zone; on the Pacific coast it is less common, and mostly grows on *Laminaria*.

The thallus of *Ectocarpus* is a branching filament which is divided into a prostrate portion, which is attached to the substratum, and an erect portion which grows upwards, supported by the water. The prostrate portion is irregularly branched, while the erect portion is profusely branched and tufted in its habit, the ends of the ultimate branches usually being narrowed to a point. The plants form a fine, thick growth on the surface of

105

the plant that bears them. Usually they do not cause serious injury, but some species of *Ectocarpus* actually penetrate the tissues of their host plant and there is good reason to believe that such species are at any rate partially parasitic.

Ectocarpus has an isomorphic alternation of generations. The spore-bearing plant or sporophyte has two kinds of sporangia, both of which are developed from the end cell of a short lateral branchlet. First, there is the type called a unilocular sporangium. The cell from which it is formed increases to several times its original size and then its nucleus divides repeatedly, forming either thirty-two or sixty-four nuclei; the initial division of the original nucleus is meiotic, so that the nuclei subsequently formed are haploid. The cytoplasm then segments round each of the nuclei, forming a zoöspore with two flagella. The zoöspores are then extruded in a mass through a small hole that opens at the end of the sporangium and, after remaining still for about a minute, they swim away in all directions.

The second type of sporangium is called a plurilocular sporangium. This also develops from an enlarged cell of a lateral branchlet, but repeated divisions of the cell result in a conical, multicellular structure. The contents of each cell form a single zoöspore and this time there is no meiosis preceding its formation, so that the zoöspores are diploid.

The subsequent development of the zoöspores depends upon whether they have come from a unilocular or a plurilocular sporangium. Haploid zoöspores from a unilocular sporangium germinate to form plants exactly similar to the preceding ones, except that they bear plurilocular sporangia *only*. From these gametes are produced; they are similar in appearance to the zoöspores, but they fuse together in pairs and form zygotes. The plant that produced them is therefore called the gametophyte. The zygotes, when they germinate, give rise to sporophytic plants bearing unilocular and plurilocular sporangia, and these in turn give rise to gametophytes, and so it goes on.

We have not yet considered the zoöspores from the plurilocular sporangia borne by the sporophyte, in addition to its unilocular sporangia. When these are formed there is no meiosis,

106

so that they are diploid, like the parent. When they germinate they produce another sporophyte. They may be regarded as an accessory means of reproducing the sporophyte generation, without first going through the gametophyte. The gametophyte, too, has its short cut in reproduction. If a gamete fails to pair with another it may none the less develop into a new plant. This development of a gamete without fertilization is called parthenogenesis, and it is not uncommon in the plant kingdom—and in certain kinds of animals, such as the plant lice or aphids ('black-fly' and 'green-fly'), too. When a gamete of *Ectocarpus* develops parthenogenetically in this way, however, it develops, not into a sporophyte, but another gametophyte, thus again 'short-cutting' the alternation of generations, this time in favour of the gametophyte.

We see that the life cycle of *Ectocarpus* is quite complicated. There is not only the regular alternation between the diploid sporophyte generation and the haploid gametophyte generations, but either generation is able to reproduce itself (but *not* the other) by accessory means: the sporophyte by the diploid spores from the plurilocular sporangia and the gametophyte by parthenogenesis. Perhaps a diagram will make it clearer.

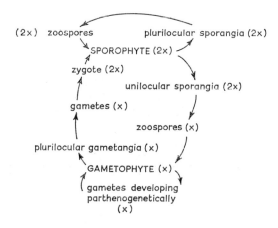

You will notice that at each stage of the cycle I have appended the chromosome number: (2x) for diploid and (x) for haploid. This brings out one thing rather clearly: although both sporophyte and gametophyte generations have their own ways of 'cheating' in the life cycle, *they cannot cheat the chromosome cycle*. The zoöspores that develop from the plurilocular sporangia on the sporophyte are still diploid, so they *must* give rise to sporophytes again; they cannot produce gametophytes. Similarly when a haploid gamete develops parthenogenetically, being haploid it must form another gametophyte. Were it not for this precaution the chromosome number of *Ectocarpus* would not be kept constant.

We thus see the alternation of generations in *Ectocarpus* as an alternation of diploid and haploid generations. This is an important biological fact, for all plants higher than the algae— all the mosses, liverworts, ferns and their allies, conifers and flowering plants—have this alternation built in as an integral part of their life histories. This is the Hofmeister cycle, discovered by Hofmeister for the fern during the last century; it can be expressed diagrammatically, very simply, like this

Ectocarpus does not always stick strictly to its alternation, for environmental factors, such as light or temperature, can affect things very much. Plants growing in British and Swedish waters, for instance, seem to be entirely sporophytic: the gametophyte never appears. In the Mediterranean near Naples, on the other hand, the gametophytic plants are much more abundant than the sporophytes, which occur but rarely. The difference probably lies in the difference of temperature, or in the stronger sunlight and clear water of the Mediterranean. In the United States, at Woods Hole in Massachusetts, both generations occur abundantly.

Ectocarpus, though it has a complicated life history, is structurally one of the simplest of the brown seaweeds. Its thallus is filamentous, and of small size. In most of the Phaeophyta the thallus is parenchymatous, consisting of more than one row of cells, forming a flattened structure. Such a one is *Dictyota*, a member of the Dictyotales. At one time the Dictyotales were thought to belong to a group of brown seaweeds quite distinct from the rest, because, unlike other Phaeophyceae, their asexual spores are not flagellated, but nowadays less significance is attached to this, especially as the antheridia of the Dictyotales are precisely similar to the gametangia of the rest of the brown seaweeds.

Dictyota has about thirty-five species, occurring mainly in the warmer seas of the world. The flat, ribbon-like thalli may be as much as a foot long in larger forms, and are attached to rocks by an irregularly shaped holdfast. *Dictyota dichotoma* is found in abundance on the southern shores of Britain, but it gets rather more infrequent as one travels north; it is also common on both the Atlantic and Pacific coasts of America.

Dictyota dichotoma is a translucent, delicate-looking plant, from four to six inches long, with the segments of its branching thallus up to one-fifth of an inch wide. The blade or lamina is only three cells thick, one layer of large, rather cubical cells being sandwiched between two layers of smaller cells. This structure makes the fronds rather delicate and limp, and they are not at all easy to spread out on blotting-paper when attempts are made to dry specimens for the seaweed collection. Its colour varies from yellowish-brown to olive-green, and careful examination reveals the reproductive bodies of a fruiting specimen as small dark brown spots scattered about the upper half of the lamina. It grows in the sublittoral zone, but it is also to be found in rock pools near to the low tide mark, where it often shows a beautiful iridescent colouring.

The growth of *Dictyota dichotoma* takes place at the tips of the branches, where there is a special cell called the apical cell. This is lens-shaped and is in a constant state of division, cutting off cells along its posterior (backward) face. Branching of the

109

thallus takes place by a vertical division of the apical cell, the two daughter cells so formed each going their own way. Branching like this, into two equal members, is called dichotomous branching; sometimes the dichotomy is hidden by the unequal growth of the two branches.

In the formation of its sex organs and the liberation of its gametes *Dictyota* is tied to the periodicity of the tides in a peculiar way. In Europe the sex organs mature every fortnight, but vary according to the situation. On the coasts of England they begin to develop during one spring tide and the gametes are set free during the next spring tide. At Naples, on the other hand, the sex organs begin their development during a neap tide and the gametes are set free during the next series of neap tides. On the Atlantic coast of North Carolina the behaviour of *Dictyota* is still more odd, for it liberates its gametes only once per lunar month, and always on the spring tides of the full moon, whether they happen to be the greater series of spring tides or not! The fortnightly periodicity of *Dictyota* is maintained even when thalli are taken away from the sea and grown in the laboratory, where all influence of the tides is removed. It is clear that the periodicity in *Dictyota* is linked with the cycle of the tides, but the manner of this linkage is by no means understood.

The sex organs are formed on either side of the thallus, in groups called sori, and male organs (antheridia) and female organs (oögonia) are produced on different plants; one can distinguish the oögonial sori by their deeper colour. Each antheridium in a male sorus is derived from a cell of the outer layer of the thallus, which divides into a stalk cell and an antheridial initial; subsequently the antheridial initial divides many times to form a multicellular antheridium, each cell of which forms a single male gamete with one flagellum. As the antheridia develop the cells immediately around the sorus grow upwards, forming a frill or involucre around the sorus.

The oögonia in a female sorus develop at first in a similar way to the antheridia, a cell of the outer layer of the thallus dividing into a stalk cell and an oögonial initial. Instead of the oögonial initial undergoing further divisions, however, it en-

110

larges very much and becomes the oögonium, containing a single egg cell. Cells surrounding the female sorus enlarge to form a rudimentary involucre, but it is not so well developed as the involucre surrounding the male sorus.

The sperms and eggs, when ripe, are set free in the sea water, and a large number of sperms gather round each egg cell like flies round a jam pot. Eventually one of them fertilizes it, and a zygote is formed.

The plant that I have just described is, of course, the gametophyte of *Dictyota*. When the zygote germinates it gives rise to the sporophyte. This is exactly similar to the gametophyte, for *Dictyota*, like *Ectocarpus*, has an isomorphic alternation of generations; instead of bearing sex organs, however, it produces sporangia. These, like the gametangia, are formed in sori on both sides of the thallus. Each sporangium in a sorus begins from a superficial cell of the thallus which first grows to two or more times its normal height and then divides crossways into a stalk cell and a sporangial cell. The sporangial cell then enlarges until it is about as wide as the thickness of the thallus, becoming spherical as it does so. Its nucleus divides twice, meiosis occurring, and the cytoplasm segments round each nucleus, forming four non-motile spores which are called tetraspores because there are four to a sporangium. The tetraspores, when they germinate, produce a new gametophyte.

The sex of the gametophytic plants is determined at the time of formation of the tetraspores, for it has been observed that, of the four spores from one sporangium, two develop into male and two into female gametophytes.

We come now to one of the most important groups of seaweeds, and one that includes the largest of the algae: the Laminariales, or kelps. The order contains about thirty genera, and they are inhabitants of the colder regions of the world. They are not found in the tropics, and even in temperate waters they grow best where the water is kept cool by cold currents. They are found close to the poles. Most of them grow below the level of low tide, and they often form submarine forests in the sublittoral zone.

111

The Laminariales have an alternation of generations that is strongly heteromorphic: the sporophyte differs profoundly in appearance from the gametophyte. In all of them it is the sporophyte that is the familiar plant, while the gametophytes are all microscopic. The gametophytes of all species so far studied are practically identical, but the sporophytes differ widely, many being noted both for their size and their complexity of structure. Among them we find the giant kelps which grow in water from thirty to a hundred feet deep, such as *Macrocystis*, the giant kelp from the Pacific coast of America, and *Nereocystis*.

The habit of growth of the kelps follows a basically similar pattern, though there are wide individual variations. The thallus is divisible into three sections; a holdfast by which it is attached to rocks below the sea, a stalk or stipe, and a blade or lamina, which may be divided into a number of long, leaf-like segments. Unlike most seaweeds, they do not grow at the ends of their branches, but instead they have a growing region at the base of the lamina, where it joins the stipe. This growing region is in an active state of cell division, renewing the blade in front and the stipe behind.

The commonest of the kelps on British shores is the oarweed (*Laminaria*), of which we have several species. It grows in the sublittoral zone, just below low tide mark, but specimens are often washed up on the shore after having been dislodged by wave action. As the blade is renewed from behind by the activity of the growing region the old blade is cast off, and quantities of the cast blades may be washed up after storms in the late spring, when they are often known as 'may weed'. Species of *Laminaria* have been given various local names, such as tangle, cow's tail, slack marrow and sea club, the last name recalling the habit of the kelp burners, who used to fight with *Laminaria* stipes as clubs.

Laminaria digitata (tangle) is a massive seaweed with a thick stipe and a well-branched lamina. The stipe, which may be from half an inch to one and a half inches in diameter, is usually from one to five feet long. At its lower end it has a large holdfast

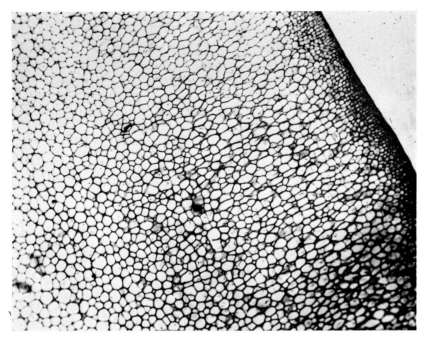

Plate 17. Part of a cross-section of the stipe of *Laminaria*

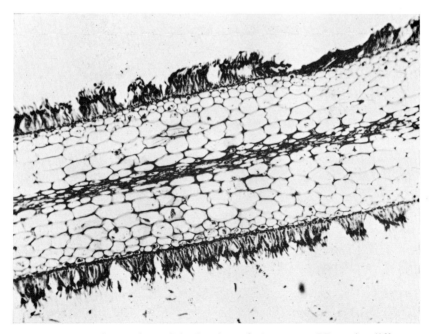

Plate 18. Part of a section of the lamina of *Laminaria*. Note the differentiation of the stipe into regions, and the sporangia on the surface

Plate 19. Fucus vesiculosus covering rocks in the middle littoral zone, Bembridge, Isle of Wight

Plate 20. Fucus serratus growing on rocks in the lower littoral zone, St. Briac, Brittany. Above the *Fucus* can be seen some fronds of *Chondrus crispus*

composed of branching strands, while the upper end is flattened
and becomes the blade, which is about the same length as the
stipe and about two feet wide. At first the blade is undivided,
but it soon becomes split into strap-like segments. The number
of segments seems to vary with the amount of buffeting to which
the blade is subjected; in exposed sites it is large, becoming
smaller in specimens from quieter water (Fig. 24).

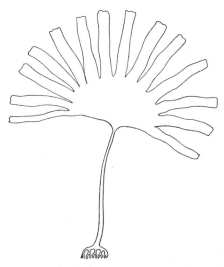

Fig. 24. Thallus of the tangle (*Laminaria digitata*).

Laminaria hyperborea (cuvie) is very similar to *L. digitata*
and in early accounts of seaweeds it was not separated from it.
The best point on which to separate the two is the structure of
the stipe. In *L. digitata* the stipe is quite smooth, whereas in
L. hyperborea it is rough, with the lower half covered with tiny
warts that produce mucilage. The rough surface of the stipe in
L. hyperborea provides a good foothold for epiphytes, so that
it is commonly found to be covered with an assortment of other
weeds, such as the red alga *Rhodymenia palmata*. *L. hypoborea*
grows at a slightly greater depth than *L. digitata*, so that the
two, when growing together, tend to form separate zones.

Laminaria saccharina (sea belt) is widespread around British coasts, growing on rocky shores in deep pools or below low tide mark. It prefers more sheltered situations than the other two species. The stipe is a foot or so long, and it bears at its end a long, narrow blade with frilled edges (Fig. 25). When

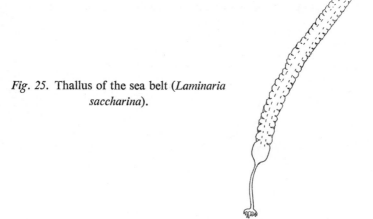

Fig. 25. Thallus of the sea belt (*Laminaria saccharina*).

dry the fronds are often covered with a whitish powder which is sweet to the taste—hence the specific epithet *saccharina*, as well as one of its popular names, which is sugar wrack. The use of the name 'wrack' for this seaweed is incorrect, as the name really belongs to members of the order Fucales. *Laminaria saccharina* is also known as the 'poor man's weather glass', because it is used to tell the weather; when dried, the fronds remain dry and brittle in dry weather, but go soft and rather sticky on the approach of rain. This behaviour is due to substances in the cell walls which absorb moisture from damp air.

The internal structure of *Laminaria* is more complex than that of any seaweed we have so far studied; in fact, the Laminariales are the most highly differentiated of all the algae. The stipe is divided into three regions: a central medulla, a cortex, and an epidermis on the outside. The medulla is composed of unbranched filaments running lengthways, with connecting filaments that run crossways. Many of the filaments that run lengthways undergo cell division as they lengthen, so that they come to be composed of rather short cells, but others undergo only occasional division, so that the cells remain long. These latter are the 'trumpet hyphae', so called because their ends are enlarged like the bell of a trumpet. It is believed that the trumpet hyphae serve to conduct dissolved food material, like the sieve tubes in the phloem of higher plants, and in some kelps, especially *Macrocystis* and *Nereocystis*, the trumpet hyphae have their end walls perforated like the bottom of a sieve, just like the sieve plates in the sieve tubes of flowering plants.

The cortex consists of radially arranged cells, packed more tightly than the medulla. The epidermis, which may be one or two cells thick, forms a continuous covering over the plant. The cells of the epidermis are smaller than those of the cortex.

The internal structure of the blade resembles that of the stipe. There is a medulla of vertical filaments and trumpet hyphae, with connecting filaments, a cortex, and an epidermis which is usually only one cell thick. Both the cells of the epidermis and the outer cells of the cortex contain numerous chloroplasts and are the cells where photosynthesis takes place.

The sporophyte of *Laminaria* is a highly complex structure, and one in which division of labour plays a considerable part; there are some cells for photosynthesis, and others for the conduction of the food that is formed, and so on. The thallus is also functionally divided into a holdfast, stipe and blade. We have come a long way from *Chlamydomonas*, where one cell had to perform all functions.

The sporangia of *Laminaria* are formed in profusion in sori that may nearly cover both sides of the frond. The sporangia are formed from epidermal cells, and they are preceded by the growth of a dense covering of hairs, called paraphyses, amongst which the sporangia are formed. Within a sporangium the nucleus divides to form either thirty-two or sixty-four nuclei, the first divisions being meiotic, and round each nucleus some cytoplasm gathers, forming a zoöspore. The zoöspores are discharged into the water and they soon begin the business of growing into gametophytes.

115

If the sporophyte of *Laminaria* is one of the most impressive of the seaweeds, the gametophyte could hardly be less conspicuous. It is filamentous and microscopic, consisting of only a few cells. The male gametophyte bears lateral branches of one or two cells on which the antheridia are formed, each antheridium being one-celled and producing a single male gamete, bearing a pair of flagella. The female gametophyte is even smaller than the male, and any of its cells is potentially capable of developing into an oögonium. The oögonium contains a single egg cell which, when ripe, is extruded through a pore in the top of the oögonium, though it still remains attached. A male gamete fuses with it, and the resulting zygote develops into a new sporophyte.

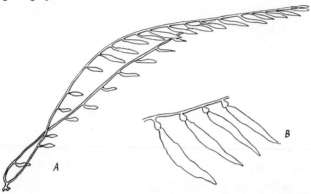

Fig. 26. The giant kelp, *Macrocystis.* A, habit of plant. B, detail of part of frond.

Other members of the Laminariales resemble *Laminaria* in their general structure, but differ in detail. The most bulky of our British seaweeds is *Saccorhiza polyschides* (furbelows), which in some cases reaches a length of fifteen feet, and a width of twelve feet across the frond. In shape it is not unlike a bulky version of *Laminaria digitata*, but it has a flattened stipe with strongly waved edges, making it impossible to mistake. *Saccorhiza* grows in the sublittoral zone, ascending to the limit of low water at spring tides, and the deeper it grows the bigger it is. In spite of its great size it is an annual.

116

Macrocystis pyrifera is the commonest of the giant kelps off the Pacific coast of the United States. This species has a branched stipe up to a hundred feet long, and forms a blade at the end of each branch, each blade having a gas bladder at its base (Fig. 26). *Nereocystis luetkiana*, another common kelp of the Pacific coast, has a stipe up to eighty feet long which ends in a large air bladder, above which a number of short branches bear each a blade about ten feet long (Fig. 27). One of the most curious of the Pacific coast kelps is *Postelsia palmaeformis*, the sea palm, which has a thick but flexible stipe about eighteen inches long, surmounted by a palm-like crown of branches, each bearing a narrow blade. It grows in the littoral zone on rocky headlands where it is exposed to the full force of the surf.

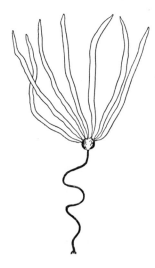

Fig. 27. Nereocystis luetkiana, showing the long stipe with a single large air bladder with long, narrow fronds attached.

The Fucales or wracks do not quite reach the dimensions of the giant kelps, but some of them, such as the great bullwracks *Durvillea* and *Sarcophycus* of subantarctic waters, attain a fair size. The wracks are our most familiar seaweeds, for many of them grow between the tide marks, and we have all had the

117

experience of walking over the great crackling masses of bladder-wrack (*Fucus vesiculosus*) that often cover the rocks by the acre.

The distribution of the Fucales is practically from pole to pole, though the larger members prefer colder waters. The greatest number of species is to be found on the coasts of Australia and New Zealand.

The genus *Fucus* occurs mainly in the littoral zone, and is the most prominent seaweed in the intertidal zone of Britain and the Atlantic coast of North America. In Britain there are three common species on the shore: the spiral wrack (*F. spiralis*), the bladderwrack (*F. vesiculosus*) and the toothed wrack (*F. serratus*). A fourth species, the horned wrack (*F. ceranoides*), occurs in estuaries and other places where the water is brackish, and occasionally the rather rare *F. anceps* may be found growing in patches on ledges on perpendicular rocks. *F. vesiculosus* is also common on the Atlantic coast of America, while on the Pacific coast *F. furcatus*, *F. membranaceus* and *F. evanescens* are found.

The structure of our three common British species of *Fucus* is very similar. There is a disk-shaped holdfast which bears a dichotomously branched thallus in the form of a flattened ribbon, with a conspicuously thickened central portion called the midrib. In *F. vesiculosus* there are gas-filled bladders scattered about the thallus which help to make it buoyant, so that when it is submerged by the tide it floats up towards the light. Air bladders are normally absent in the other two species. In *F. serratus* the edge of the blade is notched like the teeth of a saw (hence the name), while in *F. spiralis* the branches of the frond have a rather twisted appearance.

Each of the three species has its own preferences about habitat. The spiral wrack grows high up on the shore, approximately at the level of high water mark of spring tides. The bladderwrack occupies the middle zone, between the tide marks, and the toothed wrack grows near to the low tide level, and is followed in the sublittoral zone by *Laminaria*. This sorting out of different species into zones is called zonation; it is a common phenomenon amongst the algae, and we shall refer to it again

118

presently. Next time you are on a rocky shore, look for it; it can be very striking.

The thallus of *Fucus* grows by means of a single four-sided apical cell which cuts off new cells from its sides and its bottom. The mature thallus has several layers. On the outside is the meristoderm, which consists of a single layer of rectangular cells very rich in chloroplasts. Beneath this is the cortex, composed of rounder cells with fewer chloroplasts, and in the centre is the medulla which contains long filaments embedded in mucilage. Some of the filaments are thin-walled, but others have thick walls and doubtless contribute to the strength of the thallus. The cells of the medulla contain very few chloroplasts. In the region of the midrib the structure is basically the same, but the medulla is enlarged, and the number of thick-walled filaments is greater.

Fucus, like *Laminaria*, has an elaborate thallus structure and shows division of labour. Photosynthesis is concentrated in the outer tissues—the meristoderm and the cortex—while the medulla forms a framework to support the thallus and conducts away the products of photosynthesis.

When the plant is ready to reproduce the tips of the branches begin to fork rather more frequently, forming the reproductive branches which bear the receptacles on which the reproductive organs are formed. These are somewhat thickened, and covered with minute warts in the centre of which is a hole leading into the conceptacle that houses the sex organs. In the bladderwrack and the serrated wrack the male and female sex organs are on separate plants, while in the twisted wrack they are not only on the same plant, but share the same conceptacle.

The conceptacles of *Fucus* are flask-shaped chambers sunk in the tissues of the receptacle and opening by a small hole, the ostiole, to the outside. They contain a lining of hairs, known as paraphyses, which, according to some people, produce the mucilage that fills the conceptacles. The male organs or antheridia are formed on the hairs, though they may also be formed on the walls of the conceptacles. They are minute and club-shaped. Each contains at first a single nucleus which divides,

119

undergoing meiosis, and the resulting nuclei continue to divide until there are sixty-four of them, each of which forms a male gamete with a pair of flagella. The antheridium has a wall of two layers. When the gametes are ripe the outer wall ruptures and the mass of gametes, still enclosed in the inner wall, is extruded from the antheridium into the slime that fills the conceptacle; eventually it finds its way out through the ostiole. The oögonia are formed on the wall of the conceptacle, each consisting of an oögonium proper and a stalk cell. The nucleus of the oögonium divides twice, undergoing meiosis, and the resulting four nuclei divide once more, so that we end up with eight nuclei. Each becomes the nucleus of an egg cell. The wall of the oögonium has three layers. Swelling of the two inner walls bursts the outer one, and the eggs, still enclosed in the inner two walls, can pass into the sea water outside. Next the middle wall dissolves, and then finally the inner wall, and the eight eggs separate from one another and float away. In the meantime, the male gametes are set free by the dissolution of the inner wall of the antheridium, and they swim towards the egg cells, attracted by a chemical that the egg cells emit. They cluster thickly round the egg cells, causing them to spin in the water by their eagerness, and eventually fertilization takes place.

After fertilization the zygote quickly develops a gelatinous cell wall which causes it to stick to any object on which it happens to lodge. It seems that the act of becoming stuck to a solid substratum sets up a polarity in the developing zygote; a cell is cut off at the lower end, which forms the holdfast, while the upper end grows out and eventually forms the stipe and lamina of the new plant. It is not known for certain how this polarity is established, but it is generally assumed to be the effect of some growth-regulating substance, and it is thought that this substance may be auxin, the common growth-regulating substance in the higher plants, which is known to be present in the egg cells of *Fucus*. Various external factors, such as light, tem-

120

perature, hydrogen ion concentration and the presence of other zygotes also affect the polarity.

In *Fucus* there is no obvious alternation of generations, for the fertilized egg develops directly into a new gametophyte. We notice, however, that this gametophyte is diploid: meiosis takes place during the formation of the male and female gametes. It is unusual for the gametophyte of a plant to be diploid, and this, amongst other things, has led many to suppose that the 'gametangia' of *Fucus* are, in fact, sporangia.

In the microsporangium (male gametangium) the first two divisions of the nucleus are meiotic, giving rise to four haploid microspores (a microspore is a spore that, when it germinates, produces the male gametophyte). Each of these four microspores then germinates to give rise to a male gametophyte of sixteen cells, each cell of which forms an antheridium and gives rise to one male gamete. This accounts for the sixty-four male gametes of *Fucus*.

In the megasporangium (female gametangium) the first two divisions of the nucleus are again meiotic, so that four haploid megaspores are formed (a megaspore is a spore that produces a female gametophyte, and is larger than a microspore). Each megaspore forms a two-celled female gametophyte, each cell of which produces one egg cell. There are thus eight egg cells.

Whether this explanation is the true one, or whether *Fucus* is simply a brown alga with no alternation of generations and a diploid gametophyte, nobody can yet say with certainty.

There are various other wracks allied to *Fucus*, some of which are very common. The channelled wrack (*Pelvetia canaliculata*) differs from *Fucus* chiefly in having no midrib and no air bladders. The frond is distinctly concave, and when the channelled wrack is uncovered by the tide, which it is most of the time, it lies with the concave side or 'channel' downwards, so that water is trapped between the frond and the rock. This enables the plant to withstand being left high and dry for days on end without coming to any permanent harm.

We find the channelled wrack high up on the shore, above the level even of *Fucus spiralis*. High spring tides may cover it, but high neap tides often do not reach it, so that the plants may lie uncovered for a week or more. The channelled wrack may even grow above the level of high spring tides, in places where it is splashed with spray but not covered. When it has been exposed to the air for some time it becomes black and rather shrivelled, but when it is covered again it soon fills out and regains its yellow to yellowish-olive colour.

Sheep and cattle feed on the channelled wrack, cattle being especially fond of it, and in Scotland it bears the name 'cow tang'.

Another very common fucoid is *Ascophyllum nodosum*, the knotted wrack, which is seen at its best on a sheltered, gently sloping beach, where the fronds may be as much as ten feet long. It has conspicuous air bladders. The knotted wrack generally occupies a position on the shore a little above the bladder-wrack.

The knotted wrack is sometimes known as the 'sea whistle', probably because children have been known to make whistles from the air bladders. In Scotland it is called 'yellow tang' on account of the yellow colour of the receptacles on the fertile plants.

The sea thong (*Himanthalia elongata*) has a curious habit of growth. The vegetative plant is a concave 'button', from one to one and a half inches in diameter. In spring and early summer long, strap-like fertile branches grow out from the centre of the button, sometimes to a distance of eight feet. These fork repeatedly, and when ready for reproduction they become covered with brown spots. The sex organs are formed in the fertile branches which, in spite of their size, correspond to the fertile tips of the frond in *Fucus*.

The sea thong is usually found in deep pools at or below the zone occupied by the serrated wrack. The colonies are usually dense, and where it grows in the sublittoral zone the light yellow colour of the thong is in strong contrast to the darker brown of the *Laminaria*.

The brown seaweeds are a large and varied group, and many interesting forms could be described if space permitted. There is, for instance, the oyster thief (*Colpomenia peregrina*), which appeared suddenly on the south coast of Britain and the Atlantic coast of France at the beginning of the present century. Its thallus is a hollow sphere, with a group of rhizoids serving for attachment to the rocks or, more commonly, to other seaweeds. It can grow to a diameter of up to eight inches. At one time it was a great nuisance in the oyster beds at Vannes, for the plants attached themselves to oysters and lifted them from their beds by the buoyancy of the hollow fronds—hence the French name 'voleuse d'huitres'. Fortunately the *Colpomenia* was unable to compete with the coarser *Enteromorpha* in the struggle for existence which goes on all the time, even on the bed of the sea, so that it was soon reduced to a rare species. For further information about this and other species more specialized works must be consulted.

CHAPTER 11

The red seaweeds

The red seaweeds or Rhodophyta are less familiar to most people than the brown seaweeds, for they are less obvious. In the main they are deep-water seaweeds, growing from just below low tide mark down to the greatest depth possible for plant life. As we go deeper in the water light becomes dimmer, until finally it becomes too faint for photosynthesis to be profitable. At that point there can be no more seaweeds of any kind, and life becomes strictly animal. The depth at which this point is reached depends on two things: the clarity of the water and the strength of the sunlight. In the North Atlantic algae seldom grow at a greater depth than 100 feet, and the algae found at the deepest points are almost entirely red seaweeds. In the Mediterranean, on the other hand, and off the coast of Florida, where the light is stronger and the water clearer, there are plenty of algae growing down to nearly 300 feet, and the flora includes green and brown, as well as red seaweeds. The greatest depth from which algae have reliably been reported is about 600 feet.

It is thought that the red seaweeds are assisted in growing down to great depths by their colour. Light that has passed through water is coloured green, and the more water it has to penetrate the greener it is. Chlorophyll does not absorb much green light; spectroscopic examination shows that it has wide absorption bands in the red and blue-violet parts of the spectrum, but none in the green. Phycoerythrin, the colouring matter of red seaweeds, on the other hand, absorbs green light strongly, and is able to pass on some of the energy it absorbs from green light to the chlorophyll, thereby helping photo-synthesis. This colour effect is known as chromatic adaptation. The cells of most Rhodophyta have a two-layered cell wall, the inner layer being of cellulose and the outer one of pectic compounds. In most of the higher species belonging to the sub-class Florideae the cells are connected by wide openings in the cell walls through which strands of cytoplasm run. In more primitive Rhodophyta the cells may contain a single chloro-plast, and in the centre is located a dense protein body which is usually known as the pyrenoid, although it probably has little in common with the pyrenoids found in the green algae. In most of the Rhodophyta, however, there are several disk-shaped chloroplasts in each cell.

Some Florideae are iridescent, and those which are have yellowish bodies, which appear to be composed of protein, in their cells; these bodies reflect light of a short wavelength. When specimens grow in strong light the light-reflecting bodies ar-range themselves along the outer walls of the cells, while the chloroplasts take up a position along the lateral walls; if the light is weak, these positions are reversed.

The chloroplasts of all the Florideae, besides containing chlorophylls, xanthophylls and carotenes, also contain two other pigments; a red one called phychoerythrin and a blue one called phycocyanin. The proportions of phycoerythrin and phycocyanin are very variable and the algae may be coloured anything from bright red to blue.

Rhodophyta are divided into two subclasses, one of which is much larger than the other. The Bangioideae, the smaller subclass of the two, contains genera in which the thallus is generally fairly simple in structure, and the reproduction, as far as is known, is relatively uncomplicated. The Florideae, which is by far the larger group, has thalli which in most cases are relatively complex, and the reproductive process is very compli-cated indeed.

A few members of the Bangioideae are unicellular, such as *Porphyridium* and *Chroothece*. In a few others, such as *Astero-cytis smaragdina*, the single cells are joined by mucilage, so that they appear to form a filament. Most of the Bangioideae, how-ever, have thalli which are either truly filamentous or parenchymatous. An example of a parenchymatous species is *Porphyra*.

Various species of *Porphyra* grow in the sublittoral zone along the Atlantic and Pacific coasts of North America, and also in this country. It is a delicate genus, with thin, membraneous fronds which are only one, or sometimes two, cells thick; the fronds have a shimmering appearance, rather like silk.

Porphyra is well known as an edible alga, for it has a high protein content and is also rich in vitamins B and C. It has been cultivated by the Japanese for three hundred years. *Porphyra* farmers sink bundles of bamboo shoots in the mud, about six feet deep. Spores of *Porphyra* readily settle on these, and when the shoots are well covered with young plants they are raised and taken usually to an estuary, where the plants are allowed to develop. When they are finally harvested, *Porphyra* thalli are washed, chopped, and set to dry on trays. *Porphyra* is used particularly as a covering to balls of boiled rice, which are used much in the same way as rolls are in Europe.

The use of *Porphyra* as a food is by no means confined to the Orient, for 'laver bread' is prepared in England from boiled plants; this produces a kind of jelly which can then be covered with oatmeal and fried. In Ireland it is called 'sloke' and is sometimes seen in fishmongers' shops.

The most common species of *Porphyra* in this country is *P. umbilicalis*, the purple laver. The plant grows from a discoid holdfast, forming a frond which may be anything from strap-shaped to semicircular; in the strap-shaped plants the lamina may be as much as two feet long by three to four inches wide, while those with semicircular fronds have a diameter of up to eight inches. The colour is variable; typically it is a beautiful rosy purple, but it may be anything from a pale purple to olive green or even brown.

Porphyra is a very adaptable alga, growing under a variety of different conditions. It is often found in dense colonies on rocky shores, and despite the delicacy of its fronds it does not appear to suffer any harm when left high and dry by the tide, for the fronds lie flat against the rocks when uncovered, resuming their normal habit when the water returns. It is found at its best in the winter in this country, though in northern regions it is also to be seen well developed in the summer.

Another British species, *P. leucostica*, is often found growing on *Fucus* and other algae in the littoral zone. It is very like *P. umbilicalis.*

The one or two layers of cells that make up the lamina of *Porphyra* are buried in a tough gelatinous matrix (Fig. 28). In

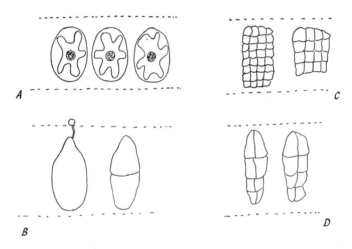

Fig. 28. Porphyra. A, three cells of thallus, embedded in gelatinous matrix. Note the large, irregularly shaped chloroplast with the nucleus in the centre. B, fertilization of a carpogonium by a spermatium which has come to rest on the outside of the gelatinous matrix. C, Segmentation of the contents of a cell to form spermatia. D, formation of carpospores from fertilized carpogonia.

most species cells contain a single chloroplast, but in a few species there are two. The lamina grows by cell division, and divisions of cells are always in a plane perpendicular to the surface, so that, although it grows in extent it does not increase in thickness.

The male reproductive cells of *Porphyra* are called spermatia, and, as in all the red algae, they have no flagella or other organs of locomotion; they rely on currents in the water to reach their destination. They are formed from vegetative cells which divide both vertically and transversely to form 16, 32, 64, or 128 spermatia. The masses of spermatia lie buried in the gelatinous matrix of the thallus. When the thallus is exposed by the out-going of the tide it dries somewhat and the matrix shrinks; when the tide comes in again the matrix swells, and this swelling presses the spermatia out of the thallus, as toothpaste is squeezed out of a tube.

The female sex organs of *Porphyra* are called carpogonia. They are only slightly modified vegetative cells. They become somewhat elongated, with an outgrowth at one end, which may or may not reach the surface of the thallus, and which functions as a trichogyne, the name given to an extension of the carpogonium on which the spermatia settle. If this reaches the surface, spermatia become attached to it in the normal way, but if it remains buried, spermatia which settle on the thallus put out very fine 'feelers' which connect with the trichogynes. The nucleus of a spermatium then passes into the trichogyne and thus to the carpogonium, where it fuses with the nucleus of the egg cell.

The fusion of the two gametes is immediately followed by division of the zygote to form from two to thirty-two carpo-spores. These are discharged, like the spermatia, when the thallus is washed by the incoming tide. They grow into filaments which, in the case of *Porphyra umbilicalis*, have been shown to be identical with the alga formerly known as *Conchocelis rosea*. This bores into the shells of marine molluscs and produces sporangia, known as monosporangia, inside the shells. Mono-spores produced by the monosporangia have not been seen to germinate, so we do not know whether they merely reproduce the *Conchocelis* stage or whether they grow into thalli of *Porphyra*.

The thallus in the Florideae is basically filamentous, but owing to the complexity of the branching, and the way that the branches are bound up together, it may have the appearance of parenchymatous growth. Careful examination, however, shows

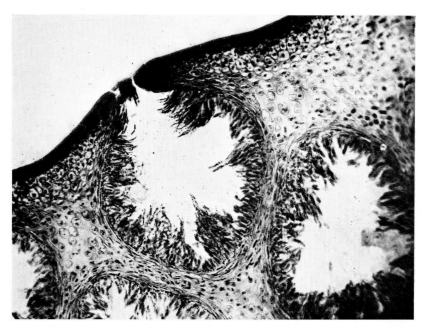

Plate 21. Section through male conceptacle of *Fucus*, showing antheridia

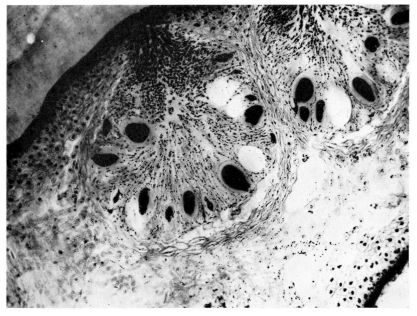

Plate 22. Section through female conceptacle of *Fucus*, showing oögonia

Plate 23. The sea oak (*Halidrys siliquosa*), Charmouth, Dorset

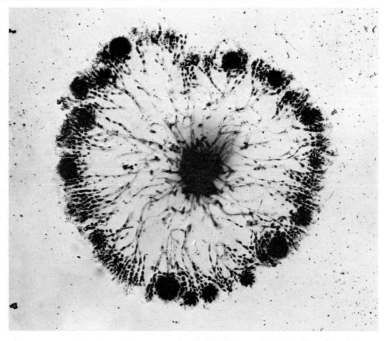

Plate 24. Section of the thallus of *Nemalion*

that, in fact, it is filamentous in nature. Such a thallus is said to be pseudoparenchymatous.

Growth always takes place by division of an apical cell at the end of a filament. There may be only one of these. Any cell of the thallus, however complex, can be traced back to its development from a single central filament; a thallus of this type is said to be monoaxial. There may, on the other hand, be several apical cells, each giving rise to its own filament, the filaments being closely woven together to form a single thallus; in this case the thallus is said to be multiaxial or to have the fountain type of organization.

A monoaxial filament grows by transverse division of the apical cell, which cuts off cells behind it as it grows forward. The cells that are cut off from the apical cell in this way soon themselves cut off lateral cells which function in the same way as the apical cell of the filament, producing a lateral branch which grows out usually more or less at right-angles to the direction of growth of the main filament. Lateral branches may produce secondary branches, and these in turn may produce other branches, forming a complex structure. The branches may be widely separated from one another, but commonly they are embedded close together in the gelatinous matrix so that a pseudoparenchyma is formed.

The cells of the Florideae, as I have already said, are connected through holes in their cell walls by protoplasmic strands, and in young portions of thallus it is possible to trace which cell developed from which by observing how these connecting strands are placed; in older portions of the thallus, however, the original connexion may become obscured by secondary connexions between cells.

A multiaxial thallus grows according to the same general plan as a uniaxial one, but instead of there being one main apical cell, each of the filaments that compose the axial cord of the thallus has its own apical cell, and no one apical cell can be said to dominate the rest. When lateral branches are developed on a multiaxial thallus they always form on the part of the filament that is not in contact with any other filament; that is to say, they develop on the outside of the thallus. A multiaxial thallus, therefore, when mature, has a structure consisting of a central portion consisting of filaments that run lengthwise (the main filaments) with a surrounding layer of lateral branches.

Usually in a multiaxial thallus the main filaments are placed in the centre of the thallus, but in some cases, especially in the Rhodymeniales, the main filaments are separate from one another, leaving a central hollow.

The thallus structure is made more complex by the fact that the cells are not necessarily of the same size; we often find, for example, an outer region or cortex formed from small cells, while the central portion or medulla may have larger cells.

Sexual reproduction in the Florideae shows a complexity that is not approached by any other group of algae, and the amount of variation between the different groups is very great. In most of them, moreover, the life-history has not been followed out in its entirety, so that we can only guess at certain of the stages.

The male sex organ or antheridium is developed on an antheridial mother cell, which is usually borne on a special filament; in more advanced Florideae the antheridial mother cells are formed in groups called sori. An antheridial mother cell forms an outgrowth which becomes an antheridium. The contents of this form a single spermatium, which is set free by the rupture of the antheridial wall, after which the antheridium may proceed to form another spermatium, and so on.

The female sex organ or carpogonium develops on a filament called the carpogonial filament, which is borne as a lateral branch of a vegetative filament; the cell that bears it is known as the supporting cell. The carpogonial filaments are usually quite short, and they can be distinguished under the microscope by the fact that they contain no chloroplasts. The carpogonium in the Florideae always has its end prolonged into a trunk-like portion called the trichogyne, which varies in length.

The male spermatium is released into the water, and water currents convey it to the trichogyne of the carpogonium, where it sticks. Its nucleus passes down the trichogyne into the carpogonium, where it fuses with the carpogonial nucleus.

It is at this point that the complications begin. In some Florideae, short filaments, known as gonimoblast filaments, grow out of the fertilized carpogonium, and at the ends of these the carposporangia containing the carpospores are formed. In more advanced genera, however, the development of the carpospores is less simple than this. The zygote nucleus, or daughter nuclei derived from it, pass first into another cell of the thallus, known as the auxiliary cell, which may be a cell of the carpogonial filament, or a supporting cell, or even a cell of the thallus some distance away from the carpogonium. In some Florideae the auxiliary cells are borne on special filaments.

The connexion between the carpogonium and the auxiliary cell, through which the zygote nucleus passes, often consists of a tubular outgrowth from the base of the carpogonium, called the oöblast. In some species the original auxiliary cell may send out oöblasts to other auxiliary cells, making the situation still more complex.

The Florideae are divided into six orders, according to the complexity of their sexual reproduction. These are: Nemalionales, Gelidiales, Cryptonemiales, Gigartinales, Rhodymeniales and Ceramiales.

The Nemalionales are the simplest order in the group. *Nemalion elminthoides* is a purplish, mucilaginous algae that grows either by itself or in small tufts. Its height is between three and ten inches. It grows from a small holdfast and forms a branched thallus about one-tenth of an inch in diameter. It is found on rocks and shells, usually in the middle part of the littoral zone, and does well in exposed places. It is an annual plant, and is usually seen from June to October in British waters.

The mature thallus is differentiated into a colourless centre and a coloured outer portion. The centre consists of filaments of rather elongated cells, which are closely interwoven one with the other. The outer sheath, or cortex, consists of short, branched filaments which end in hairs.

Both male and female reproductive organs are borne on the

same plant, though it may seem otherwise, because they seldom occur at the same time. The antheridial branches can be distinguished from vegetative branches because their cells contain no chloroplasts, or, at the most, poorly developed ones with little pigment. They consist of from four to eight cells, each of which is an antheridial mother cell. Each mother cell usually forms four antheridia, and each antheridium contains a single spermatium which when ripe is set free by a break in the antheridial wall. After the escape of the spermatium another may develop in the old antheridium.

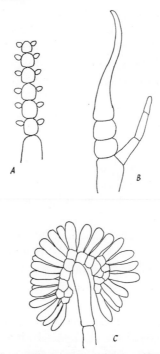

Fig. 29. Nemalion. A, male filament with antheridia. B, Carpogonial branch with carpogonium. C, developing carposporangia.

The carpogonial filament develops from a cell near the base of a lateral branch. This initial cell forms usually three daughter cells. The end cell of a carpogonial branch develops into a carpogonium with an elongated trichogyne (Fig. 29).

The spermatium, carried by water currents, drifts against the trichogyne of the carpogonium. Soon after it lodges there the nucleus of the spermatium divides into two, and one or both nuclei pass into the trichogyne. One of them goes on to the carpogonium and there fuses with the female nucleus.

The zygote nucleus, after enlarging somewhat, divides by meiosis into two daughter nuclei, one beneath the other. The lower nucleus takes no further part in the proceedings and ultimately disappears, but the other nucleus divides, and one of the two daughter nuclei passes into a branch that grows out from the cell containing it. A cell wall forms, cutting off the protuberance, which then becomes the first cell of a gonimoblast filament. Several other filaments are developed in the same way from the original cell. At the end of each filament a carposporangium is formed. When the carpospores are ripe the walls of the carposporangia burst and they are set free; often new carpospores are then formed in the old carposporangium. The carpospore becomes fixed to a submerged rock and germinates, developing into a new plant of *Nemalion*.

The life history of *Nemalion* is about as simple as any life history can be in the Florideae. It shows an alternation of generations. The main plant, which bears the sex organs, is the gametophyte. The gonimoblast filaments, with their carposporangia, are known as the carposporophyte. In *Nemalion*, as far as we know, the carpospores germinate to form new gametophytes again, but in most Florideae there is an additional sporophyte generation, known as the tetrasporophyte, before we get back to the gametophyte.

The Gelidiales show an advance on the Nemalionales in having a tetrasporophyte generation in the life history. They are still primitive, however, in that the carposporophyte develops directly from the carpogonium without the intervention of auxiliary cells as in some of the higher Florideae.

Species of *Gelidium* are of great economic importance as one of the chief sources of agar. *Gelidium corneum* is a common seaweed in the littoral zone, often found under overhanging rocks or at the edges of rock pools. It is commonest in the southern half of the British Isles, but extends to the extreme north of Scotland. It has a horny, rather rigid texture, and its colour varies from crimson to purple; it is rather translucent in appearance. Its fronds are from one to three inches high, and it usually grows in close colonies, rather like a turf. The branches of its thallus vary from flat to cylindrical, and the length of the branches also varies very much.

Gelidium is a perennial plant which grows from a persistent basal portion each season. There is an axial filament consisting at first of a single line of cells. Each cell of the original filament forms four cells known as pericentral cells which surround it; each pericentral cell then produces a short lateral filament, and the tips of the filaments lie close together, forming a pseudoparenchymatous thallus.

The antheridia are borne in groups or sori on the branches of the male plant. An antheridial mother cell usually carries two antheridia.

Carpogonial filaments are likewise borne on fertile branches, usually near the growing point. The carpogonial filament consists of a single cell which becomes modified into a carpogonium with a long trichogyne. Spermatia carried by water currents become attached to the trichogyne in the usual way and the egg cell in the carpogonium is fertilized. From the fertile carpogonium gonimoblast filaments grow out and form numerous one-celled lateral branches, each of which becomes a carposporangium. It seems likely that the mass of interwoven gonimoblast filaments had their origin from several fertile carpogonia, but they are so mixed up together that one really cannot see precisely where they have come from.

The germination of the carpospores of *Gelidium* has not been followed out completely, but there can be no doubt that they develop into the tetrasporophyte generation. This is precisely similar to the gametophyte generation, but it bears tetrasporangia on its fertile branches instead of sex organs. Each tetrasporangium contains four tetraspores; at first it has one nucleus, but this divides by meiosis into four, each daughter nucleus becoming the nucleus of a tetraspore. Germination of the tetraspores is presumed to give rise to the gametophyte generation again.

The Cryptonemiales have an additional complication in their sexual reproduction in that they have an auxiliary cell borne on a special auxiliary filament, which may be developed on the supporting cell of a carpogonial filament or may be some distance from it. After fertilization, the zygote nucleus or one of its descendants migrates from the carpogonium into a cell of the carpogonial filament, which is called the nurse cell. Oöblasts then grow from the nurse cell to the auxiliary cell, through which nuclei pass, and the auxiliary cell then gives rise to gonimoblast filaments and carposporangia.

The Cryptonemiales are a fairly large order, comprising about 85 genera and 650 species. A particularly interesting family is the Corallinaceae, in which the thallus is thoroughly impregnated with lime and magnesia, making it hard and brittle to the touch. It is small wonder that these strange calcareous seaweeds were at first classified with the corals. They were not, in fact, distinguished from them until the middle of last century. They usually have a pinkish colour, owing to the colour combination of white lime with red or purple chloroplasts. Their reproductive organs are formed in flask-shaped cavities or conceptacles, superficially resembling the conceptacles found in the Fucales.

These calcareous algae are of great importance in reef building. The great part they play in the building of 'coral islands' in the Pacific was recognized only from the beginning of the century, although their remains in the rocks date from the Cretaceous period. Borings made on the island of Funafuti, in the South Pacific, to a depth of more than 1,000 feet, showed clearly that calcareous algae rather than corals were the chief organisms responsible for the growth of the island. It is now known that many 'coral' reefs and 'coral' islands are built entirely, or almost entirely, of these calcareous algae, and in many atolls in the South Seas growth is still going on by the deposition of lime through the activity of seaweeds.

It must not be thought that the calcareous seaweeds are only

135

found in tropical seas, however, for several species occur on the coasts of Britain. *Corallina officinalis* is very common on rocky shores all round the British Isles, mostly growing on rocks in shallow pools or on fairly gently sloping rocks towards low water mark. It revels in an exposed situation, but its great enemy is desiccation. The plant has a tufted habit of growth, a thallus from one to five inches high being developed from a holdfast which is hard and calcareous. The thallus is cylindrical, consisting of lime-encrusted segments not much longer than they are broad. The plant branches freely in its upper portions, producing a more or less fan-shaped growth.

Corallina squamata is even more common than *C. officinalis* in the southern part of England and in Ireland; the two plants are very much alike and are difficult to separate from one another. Also abundant in the southern half of Britain is *Jania rubens*, the tufts of which, from half an inch to one and a half inches high, with a delicate rosy colour, are very beautiful. The thallus is jointed like that of *Corallina*, but the segments are longer and narrower, seldom being wider than a thread of cotton. *J. rubens* usually grows on other algae, especially *Cladostephus*, from the mid-littoral zone down to the sublittoral.

Mesophyllum lichenoides is less common, but it is found from time to time, chiefly in the south of England and in Ireland. It is sometimes found growing on *Corallina*. Its thallus looks rather like a shell, about one inch in diameter and no more than one-fiftieth of an inch in thickness. It is rose-pink in colour, with a white margin.

Lithophyllum encrustans is very common indeed in rocky pools in the littoral zone. It is what is known as a crustaceous coralline seaweed; it grows as a solid crust, usually with a rather irregular surface, often half an inch or so in thickness, and its colour varies from rose-violet to yellowish-mauve according to whether it is growing in the shade or in the open. *Lithothamnion lenormandi* is a similar species, almost equally common, which grows preferably in the shade; it is typically seen in rocky crevices and on rocks which are well covered with *Fucus*. It is usually of a reddish-violet colour, and can be distinguished from

Lithophyllum encrustans by its white margin, which is slightly thickened and lobed.

The Gigartinales include the well-known carragheen 'moss' (*Chondrus crispus*), also known as 'Irish moss'. This is a seaweed that grows in rock pools of the lower littoral zone, extending down into the sublittoral. It gets its name 'Irish moss' from its frequency on the Irish coast, where it is still used as a food. More than a century ago it became popular as a medicine, especially for coughs, infusions being drunk either with cocoa or with lemon or other flavours. It is also used in making jellies and blancmanges.

Chondrus crispus is a perennial plant, forming clusters of fronds growing from a holdfast. Growth is very variable. Near the holdfast it is compressed, but it gradually expands into a frond up to one inch wide, which branches dichotomously.

During the last war, when supplies of agar were running short, a team of biologists and chemists was asked by the Ministry of Supply to find some British seaweed which could be used to supply agar instead of Japanese material, and, after much experimentation, *Gigartina stellata* was found not only to give a good agar, but also—an important point—to be present on our shores in a quantity sufficient for our needs.

G. stellata grows at about the level of low spring tides, where it may cover a large area. It occurs all round the British Isles, but is commonest on the west coast. It is a dark, purplish red plant which grows in thick tufts, three to six inches high, from a disk-shaped holdfast. The fronds are narrowed at the base, but they expand somewhat higher up and become ribbon-like, though they seldom reach a width greater than a quarter of an inch. There are, however, broader examples in which the ends of the fronds are up to three-quarters of an inch across. The plants may well be confused with *Chondrus crispus*, but can be distinguished by their dark colour.

There are about ninety species of *Gigartina*, widely distributed in the Atlantic and Pacific Oceans. Twenty-eight species occur on the Pacific coast of North America, but only one species is found on the Atlantic coast. Most species are perennial.

The fronds are very variable; they may be cylindrical or flattened, undivided or branched in various ways.

Gracilaria verrucosa is another seaweed of economic importance for the production of agar. It grows in considerable abundance off the coast of South Australia, and during the last war a great deal of it was used as a gelatinous packing for canned meat.

The Rhodymeniales are an interesting order in which the thallus is frequently hollow, owing to the axial filaments cut off behind the apical initials lying in a hollow cylinder instead of a solid one, as in most multiaxial Florideae. Various species occur round the British coasts. The dulse (*Rhodymenia palmata*) is a largish, purple-red seaweed which produces tufts ten to twelve inches high, growing from a disk-shaped holdfast. It often grows in quantity on the oarweeds in the sublittoral zone, and is also found on the lower part of the shore, growing on the serrated wrack and other seaweeds, or on rocks.

The dulse, which is known as dillisc in Ireland, is a well-known edible seaweed, being chewed like tobacco after having been washed and dried. It is said to be an excellent panacea for the after-effects of seasickness. It is sometimes eaten fresh in salads, but the fronds are very tough and do not have much flavour. The mountain sheep in north-west Scotland come down to the shore at low tide and graze on the fronds of *Rhodymenia palmata*. The Norwegians know the dulse as sheep's weed.

Gastroclonium ovatum grows on rocks in the lower littoral zone, and is often found in the south of England. The plants are bushy, purple or reddish in colour, and grow from three to six inches high from a disk-shaped holdfast. The frond is tough and cylindrical, about one-twenty-fifth of an inch in diameter, and profusely branched. The branches bear numerous small bladders, which look like leaves. The 'leaves' may drop off during the summer, but are replaced by more.

The Ceramiales are an important order containing about 160 genera and about 900 species. The best-known member of the order is *Polysiphonia*, which has the distinction of being one of the very few red algae in which the carpospores have been seen to grow into tetrasporophytes and the tetraspores have similarly been watched growing into gametophytes. Its life history is therefore known in all its details, and nothing is left to guess-work. *Polysiphonia* is a common seaweed round British shores, and on both Atlantic and Pacific coasts of the United States.

Plants of *Polysiphonia* have thalli in the form of branched filaments, and the name *Polysiphonia* comes from the fact that the thallus is so constructed that the central filament is surrounded by a number of longitudinally arranged filaments or 'siphons'.

The young thallus grows from a single apical cell, which cuts off a line of axial cells behind it. Each axial cell then forms a layer of pericentral cells surrounding it, and the number of pericentral cells is more or less constant for any given species, and varies from four to twenty-four. Besides forming pericentral cells, the axial cell may produce branched, tapering filaments. These may repeat the 'polysiphoneous' structure of the main axis, or they may be monosiphoneous, without pericentral cells, in which case they are called trichoblasts. The cells of a trichoblast are usually colourless, or at most very faintly coloured.

The sexual reproduction of *Polysiphonia* is extremely complex. The antheridia are formed upon special fertile trichoblasts near the apex of the thallus. A fertile trichoblast, as it develops,

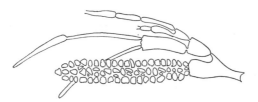

Fig. 30. Polysiphonia. Male fertile trichoblast with antheridia. (After Yamanouchi, modified)

branches dichotomously, and in most species of *Polysiphonia* one arm develops into the fertile axis, which is short, while the other develops into a long, branched sterile axis (Fig. 30).

The fertile axis is unbranched and several cells long. The bottom two cells are sterile, while the others each form a number

139

of pericentral cells surrounding them, and each pericentral cell then cuts off one or more antheridial mother cells.

The female sex organs are formed on a fertile trichoblast of the female plant. The fertile trichoblast is usually five to seven cells in length, the two lowermost cells being surrounded by pericentral cells. One of the pericentral cells in the uppermost of the two layers is the supporting cell of the carpogonial filament. From it grows a four-celled carpogonial filament, of which the end cell becomes a long, erect trichogyne (Fig. 31). During the development of the carpogonial filament, two sterile filament initials are cut off from the supporting cell, one from its base and the other on one side.

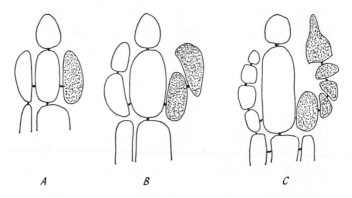

A   *B*   *C*

Fig. 31. Fertile trichoblast of *Polysiphonia*, showing development of the carpogonial filament (shaded). (After Yamanouchi, modified)

Fertilization now occurs by a spermatium becoming attached to the trichogyne and its nucleus passing down the trichogyne into the carpogonium. Shortly after fertilization the lateral sterile filament initial divides to form a filament of from four to ten cells. Then the supporting cell cuts off a daughter cell on its upper side, and this cell is the auxiliary cell. It lies just below the base of the carpogonium, and very soon becomes connected with it by a tube (Fig. 32). A daughter cell of the fertilized zygote nucleus passes into the auxiliary cell, and then a compact mass of gonimoblast filaments grows out of the top of the auxiliary

140

cell. The end cells of these filaments develop into carposporangia. During the development of the carposporophyte, the supporting cell, the auxiliary cell, and cells of the sterile filaments fuse to form a single placental cell, and the surrounding vegetative cells begin to divide and ultimately form a large, urn-shaped pericarp, with an opening, or ostiole, at one end, which envelops the developing fruit body.

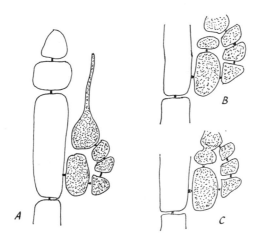

Fig. 32. Carpogonial filament of *Polysiphonia* after fertilization, showing development of the auxilliary cell (shaded). (After Yamanouchi, modified)

Carpospores set free from the carposporangia have been seen to develop into tetrasporophytes, which resemble the gametophytes. The tetrasporangia are developed from pericentral cells, and in each tetrasporangium the nucleus divides by meiosis and four tetraspores are formed. The tetraspores, when ripe, are set free by the sporangium wall rupturing, and they germinate and develop into gametophyte plants.

The red seaweeds are a large and a complex group of plants that would require a book on their own to do them justice. They are particularly remarkable for their very complex life history, in which, in most genera, the gametophyte generation is followed by two distinct sporophytes—the carposporophyte, consisting of the gonimoblast filaments and their carposporangia, and the tetrasporophyte. The tetrasporophyte is usually similar to the gametophyte, but the carposporophyte is totally different, and is parasitic on the gametophyte.

Another feature of the red algae is that they have no motile cells in their life history—not even the spermatia or male gametes have flagella. The only other major group of algae that are entirely without flagellated cells of any kind are the blue-green algae or Cyanophyta, which we shall meet in the next chapter. This lack of cells with flagella has suggested to some people that the two groups are distantly related, a view that has been strengthened by the fact that the blue-green pigment phycocyanin is common to both groups. Any such relationship, however, if it exists at all, lies hidden in antiquity; if the Rhodophyta and the Cyanophyta really are related, then one group must have split off from the other at a very early date. Our earliest fossil records of Rhodophyta belong to algae of the Ordovician age, but the group must be much older than that. For lack of any positive evidence one way or another, it is perhaps best to regard them as a class on their own, and not related with any other group.

CHAPTER 12

The blue-green algae

The blue-green algae or Cyanophyta, the last group that we have to consider, differ from the rest of the algae in a number of important ways. Their pigments, instead of being contained in chloroplasts, are dispersed throughout the outer layers of the cytoplasm of the cells. These pigments include chlorophyll *a*, various carotenes and xanthophylls, as well as phycoerythrin and phycocyanin, which occur in varying amounts in the different species. Another important difference between the Cyanophyta and the rest of the algae is the absence of a proper nucleus, though there is a 'central body' which appears to control cell activities. The Cyanophyta also lack flagellated reproductive cells, and there appears to be no sexual process in any member of the group.

The Cyanophyta are a very primitive group of algae. As we have seen (Chapter 1), there were probably Cyanophyta on the earth in pre-Cambrian times, more than five hundred million years ago, and many species living today may well be very similar to those far-off pioneers that were among the first plants to appear in the sea. In spite of their ancient lineage and primitive characters, however, we cannot say that they are an unsuccessful group, even if they have not produced any complex descendants. There are today about 150 genera, containing something like 1,500 species, with a very varied distribution. Some live in the sea, many more inhabit fresh water, and there are also many common species that live in the soil. Some species inhabit the water in hot springs all over the world, the highest temperature that they are known to tolerate being 85°C—only 15° short of the boiling-point. Possibly their simple structure helps them to resist high temperatures.

An interesting feature of the life of some of the blue-green algae in hot springs is the way in which they precipitate salts of calcium and magnesium from the hot water. In those springs in which the water is heavily charged with bicarbonates of calcium and magnesium, the growth of blue-green algae causes precipitation of the carbonates. This gives rise to a material called travertine, which may be precipitated so fast as to gain 4 millimetres in thickness in a week. Terraces of travertine, coloured by the algae that grow on them, form a characteristic and beautiful sight in many hot springs.

Some of the fresh-water Cyanophyta are members of the plankton, and are specially numerous in the warmer months of the year. At this time some species become so abundant that they colour the water, and are then known as 'water-blooms'; in some places the development of a water-bloom is an annual occurrence.

Many fresh-water species are partly terrestrial, growing on ledges where water drips and similar places. Terrestrial Cyanophyta are usually fairly inconspicuous, but in certain circumstances they may form quite a distinct slimy coating on the surface of the soil.

Most of the marine Cyanophyta are found in the intertidal zone. Some of them are free-living, but most of them grow on, or sometimes even in, other algae.

The Cyanophyta contains only one class, the Cyanophyceae, or Myxophyceae. They are all microscopic.

Some of the Cyanophyta are unicellular, but more usually, when cell division takes place, the daughter cells do not separate but form a colony. These may be either filamentous or non-filamentous. In a non-filamentous colony the individuals are held together by the gelatinous sheath that usually surrounds the cells of Cyanophyta, the shape of the colony depending on how the cells divide; it may be a flat plate, a hollow sphere, or an amorphous mass of cells.

Many of the Cyanophyta have the form of filaments, rather

144

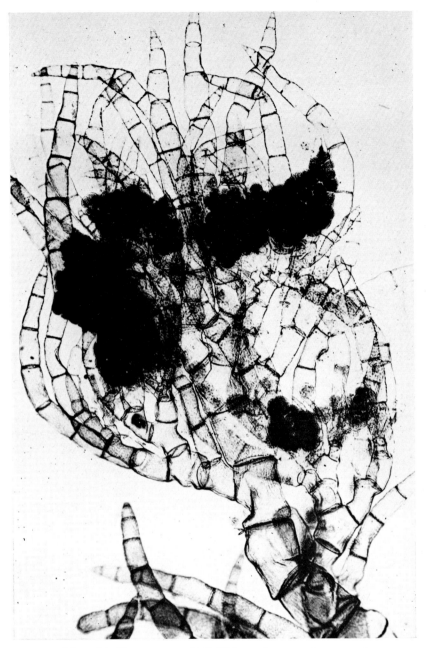

Plate 25. Cystocarps of *Callithamnion*, a red seaweed

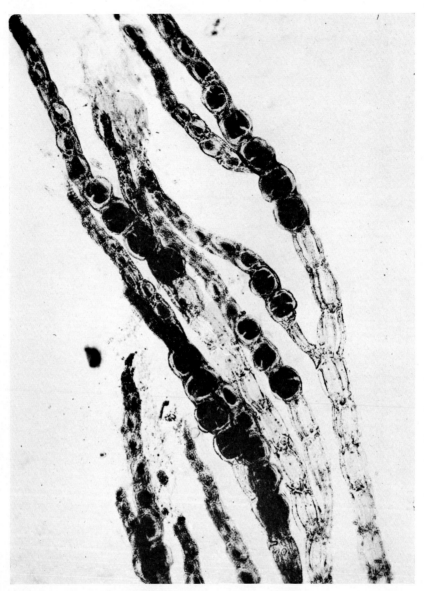

Plate 26. Branches of the thallus of *Polysiphonia* with tetraspores

like the filaments of *Spirogyra*, but they, too, are regarded as colonies rather than true filaments. A single row of cells in a filament is called a trichome, and a filament may consist of one trichome or of several. In *Nostoc* and *Anabaena* the rounded cells that make up the filament look rather like beads strung together, while in *Oscillatoria* and *Rivularia* the filament has straight sides (Fig. 33).

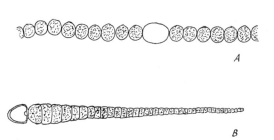

Fig. 33. Blue-green algae. A, part of a filament of *Anabaena*. B, *Rivularia*.

The cell wall is generally composed of two layers, the inner layer being firm and the outer layer more or less gelatinous. The gelatinous sheath is often coloured yellow, red, brown or violet. Where the coloration is yellow or brown it is usually caused by a mixture of two pigments called fuscorhodin and fuscochlorin, while if it is red or violet it is commonly due to the pigment gleocapsin. Since the algal cells themselves contain phycoerythrin (red) and phycocyanin (blue), as well as chlorophyll, the possibilities of colour in the blue-green algae are almost infinite. In actual fact, this possibility is seldom realized, and most of the Cyanophyta are a rather dull blue-green.

It has long been recognized that the protoplasm in the cells of Cyanophyta consists of an outer and an inner portion. The outer portion, which is called the chromoplasm, contains the pigments. It also contains numerous granules of various kinds, amongst which we can recognize granules of carbohydrate of some kind, which acts as a store of reserve food. The nature of the carbohydrate is uncertain. According to some authorities it is identical with the glycogen that is found as a food reserve in many animal cells, but according to others the granules consist of a carbohydrate nearer to starch than glycogen. This carbohydrate is often called cyanophycean starch. In addition, the chromoplasm contains granules, known as cyanophycin granules, which appear to be protein.

The inner colourless portion of the protoplasm, or central body, has puzzled cytologists ever since its existence was first demonstrated. Its reaction to stains makes it clear that it contains chromatin, the material to be found in normal nuclei. On the other hand, the central body is not organized in the way that normal nuclei are: it contains no nucleoli, the deeply staining bodies that are found in other nuclei, nor is it bounded by any definite nuclear membrane. Some people think that the nuclear material is concentrated at certain points in a protoplasmic network, while others hold that it is more generally distributed throughout the central body. Probably it varies with the species. There has been much difference of opinion upon the manner in which the central body undergoes division, some authorities believing that there is a spindle which in general resembles the spindle formed during mitotic division of a normal nucleus, while others hold that division of the central body is of a primitive type in which mitosis plays no part.

Another difference of opinion arises about the nature of the bodies which have been called gas vacuoles that are often present in planktonic species of Cyanophyta. These appear as dark-coloured bodies under the microscope, often present in such quantity that the other cell contents are obscured. Some experiments seem to indicate that gas vacuoles disappear when the algal cells are placed in a vacuum, bubbles of gas appearing at the same time at the surface of the cells. It does seem that these structures are vacuoles filled with gas, and the gas is thought to be nitrogen, but their function, if any, is unknown. Possibly the gas vacuoles give the algae buoyancy in the water.

The trichomes of many filamentous blue-green algae have the power of movement, which may consist of a gliding motion of the whole trichome, or a slow movement to and fro of the

146

end of a trichome, as if the alga were wagging its tail. The movement is particularly noticeable in hormogonia, the fragments into which filaments break up on reproduction. Some species, such as *Oscillatoria*, show both the gliding and the waving movements.

What it is that gives the motile blue-green algae their power of movement is uncertain, but it seems likely that it may be due to the secretion of gelatinous material through tiny pores in the cell wall. Some people, however, think that the movement is due not to secretion of gelatinous material but to waves of expansion and contraction passing along the filament.

There has been a certain amount of argument about whether certain species of blue-green algae can 'fix' atmospheric nitrogen —that is, cause it to combine to form compounds so that it ultimately becomes available for the nourishment of other plants. Most of the early work is questionable, as the precautions taken to make quite certain that the cultures used in experiments were quite free from bacteria were inadequate. More lately, however, it has been convincingly shown that certain of the Cyanophyta can grow in a culture solution that does not contain any nitrogen compounds, and, moreover, combined nitrogen appeared in the medium after they had been growing for a time. This seems to indicate that they are getting nitrogen from the atmosphere, a view which has been confirmed by the use as a tracer of the radioactive heavy isotope of nitrogen N^{15}. This is a form of nitrogen chemically identical with the nitrogen of the air, but with an atomic weight of 15 instead of 14. If a nitrogen-fixing blue-green alga is supplied with air containing a certain amount of the heavier isotope, it can be shown by tests for radioactivity that the isotopic nitrogen has entered the body of the alga.

Although certain species of Cyanophyta have been shown to fix nitrogen under experimental conditions, it is still doubtful how much they fix, if any, in Nature. Experiments appear to indicate that they do not fix atmospheric nitrogen if they are supplied with nitrogen in the form of nitrates or ammonium salts as an alternative. It seems to be fairly well established, however, that some species do fix nitrogen in the soil. In the paddy fields in which rice is grown in the Far East the soil is flooded in the wet season, and while it is inundated a thick growth of *Nostoc* appears. In the course of about six weeks this *Nostoc* is said to fix 70 lb of nitrogen per acre—an amount equivalent to 3 cwt of nitrate of soda fertilizer. It seems probable that nitrogen fixed by the blue-green algae does, in certain habitats at any rate, play a very real part in the economics of Nature.

Reproduction in the Cyanophyta is very simple. In non-filamentous species the normal method is by cell division, the two daughter cells usually remaining fixed to one another by a common gelatinous envelope, so that rapid cell division results in a colony of many cells. If the gelatinous material joining the cells is soft it tends to dissolve away, with the result that the colony never gets very large, but if it is more resistant the colony may achieve considerable size before it breaks up.

In filamentous species the trichomes eventually break up. This may result from the death of certain cells in the row, leaving a weak point, or from material joining the cells being weaker at some points than at others. In particular, there is often a weak junction between the filaments and certain specialized cells called heterocysts; these are usually larger than the other cells in the filament, and they have such transparent contents that they appear to be empty. Where heterocysts occur, they are often associated with the breaking up of the filament into short sections or hormogonia. These hormogonia have greater power of motility than the filaments that gave rise to them, so that they move away from the parent filament and eventually grow into new filaments on their own.

Many filamentous Cyanophyta give rise to non-motile spores called akinetes. These simply consist of cells of the filament in which there has been an accumulation of food reserves; the cell usually enlarges and develops a thicker wall. These akinetes appear to be resting spores with the function of enabling the algae to survive unfavourable periods, and usually they germinate, giving rise to new filaments, when things become more favourable. They have been known to remain viable for as long as seventy years.

Some of the Cyanophyta produce endospores, the contents of the cell dividing up into a large number of small bodies. Those species that form endospores are placed in the order called Chamaesiphonales.

CHAPTER 13

How algae live

Compared with the vast amount of work that has been done on the physiology of the higher plants, our knowledge of the physiology of algae is comparatively slender. Certain aspects have, however, been studied fairly intensively; in particular, the unicellular green algae *Chlorella* and *Scenedesmus* have proved particularly favourable subjects for work on photosynthesis.

A description of the mechanism of photosynthesis does not fall into the scope of this book, and the reader who is interested should consult a work on plant physiology; I particularly recommend that excellent book *The Growth of Plants*, by G. E. Fogg, published by Penguin Books. Briefly, the process of photosynthesis consists of the building up of sugar from carbon dioxide and water, by the aid of sunlight and the green pigment, chlorophyll. This requires the reduction of the carbon-dioxide molecule, which in turn needs energy, and the energy of sunlight is trapped by the chlorophyll and made available for chemical work.

The carbon dioxide is reduced, after being 'fixed' or brought into combination with something in the plant, by hydrogen from water. In order that this may happen the water must first undergo photolysis: that is, it must be split up into its elements by light energy. The hydrogen can then be used to reduce the combined carbon dioxide, while the oxygen, which is not needed, is given off as a by-product. The water is called a hydrogen donor because it supplies hydrogen. The reduced carbon dioxide is built into phosphoglyceric acid, which, by a further complex series of changes, becomes sugar. The whole process is extremely complicated—too much so to be adequately summarized in a few words.

We have no reason to believe that the photosynthetic process in algae, and particularly the green algae, differs essentially from what takes place in the higher plants; hence the extensive use of algal cultures in research on photosynthesis. Some algae, however, possess other pigments than chlorophyll, and the part played, if any, by these pigments in photosynthesis has at times been hotly debated.

Chlorophyll exists in several related forms, known as chlorophyll *a*, chlorophyll *b* and so on. The chloroplasts of higher plants contain four pigments: chlorophyll *a*, chlorophyll *b*, and two yellow-orange pigments called xanthophyll and carotene. Of these, the chlorophyll *a* is the pigment primarily concerned with photosynthesis, but there is good evidence that the other pigments can help in the process.

'White' light really consists of all the colours of the rainbow mixed together; this can be proved by passing it through a prism, which analyses it into its constituent colours. Chlorophyll does not absorb all colours equally. Red and blue light waves are absorbed readily, but green is hardly absorbed at all, and so is reflected—hence the green colour of chlorophyll. It is possible, however, for light waves of a wavelength unsuitable for absorption by chlorophyll *a* to be absorbed by xanthophyll, the energy they contain being then transferred from the xanthophyll molecule to the chlorophyll *a*. In this way photosynthetic activity is not limited to the light that can be absorbed directly by chlorophyll *a*.

This energy transference can be beautifully demonstrated in the laboratory by illuminating a mixture of chlorophyll and xanthophyll with light of a wavelength absorbed by xanthophyll but not by chlorophyll. In spite of its inability to absorb the light, the chlorophyll becomes fluorescent, glowing with a deep red light. This could only happen if the chlorophyll molecules were excited by the energy absorbed by the xanthophyll and passed on to them.

In the green algae (Chlorophyta) the chlorophyll pigments

151

are much the same as in higher plants, but in other groups this is not so. Not only are there other variants of the chlorophyll molecule—chlorophyll *c*, chlorophyll *d* and chlorophyll *e*—but various other pigments also occur. Even amongst the Chlorophyta there is quite a wide range of variation between the pigmentation of various species, especially in the xanthophylls that they contain. The words 'xanthophyll' and 'carotene' are convenient terms for a whole series of related pigments; there are at least seventeen xanthophylls and four carotenes found in different groups of algae, and of these, eight of the xanthophylls and all the four carotenes are found in one or another of the Chlorophyta.

Besides the xanthophylls and carotenes, the chloroplasts of the Rhodophyta and Cyanophyta may contain phycoerythrin or phycocyanin or both. These pigments belong to the class of substances called phycobilins, and we know less about them than we do about the other pigments. This is in part due to their more complex structure. The phycobilins are proteins with molecular weights in excess of 250,000; unlike the chlorophylls, xanthophylls and carotenes, they are insoluble in fat solvents such as alcohol or acetone, but soluble in water. Both phycoerythrin and phycocyanin exist in more than one form. Phycoerythrin is coloured red, while phycocyanin is blue. Both are strongly fluorescent: that is, they behave like a television screen, glowing when struck by radiation of a certain wavelength. Fluorescence is often an indication that a substance is photochemically active.

In spite of the great variety of pigments amongst the algae, the chief photosynthetic pigment in all of them is chlorophyll *a*. This is often regarded as a sign that they had a common origin in evolution, for it looks as if either the ability to use chlorophyll for photosynthesis arose only once in the history of the earth, or that only plants with a chlorophyll system managed to survive. Certain bacteria—the so-called purple bacteria—manage to carry out photosynthesis with the help of a purple pigment, but bacteria are notoriously peculiar in their chemistry.

When sunlight enters water most of the red rays are quickly absorbed, leaving the blue and blue-green rays to be transmitted. The blue component of sunlight is relatively weak, while the blue-green is intense, so that it is mainly the blue-green light that is available for photosynthesis in a submerged marine plant. Blue-green light, however, is poorly absorbed by chlorophyll a. We have the paradox, therefore, that the main photosynthetic pigment of the algae does not absorb well in the wave band of the light that reaches them in greatest quantity. This gave rise to the idea of chromatic adaptation.

By chromatic adaptation we mean the development in the chloroplast of pigments with colours complementary to that of the chlorophyll, so that light not absorbed by the chlorophyll can be taken in by the accessory pigments and made available for photosynthesis. It is an attractive idea, and its devotees were quick to point out that the red algae, in which chromatic adaptation presumably reached its most perfect expression, were mainly inhabitants of deep water. Indeed, it has been shown that the phycobilins in red algae, as well as the fucoxanthin in brown algae and the carotenoid pigments in various green algae, do, in fact, absorb light that can be used for photosynthesis. Before the case for chromatic adaptation can be considered proved, however, we should take a look at the other side of the story.

The absorption of blue-green light by chlorophyll a is certainly very poor, but the percentage of incident light that is absorbed by a plant depends on a lot of things besides the spectral properties of the absorbing pigment. Increased concentration of chlorophyll in the cells, for instance, would mean that more of the light could be absorbed, and the depth of the photosynthetic layer would also have its effect. Taking all these things into account, one could well imagine a deep-water plant whose chloroplasts contained nothing but chlorophyll a, but which could still absorb all the blue-green light that reached it. The development of complementary pigments by such a plant would have little, if any, survival value. It is therefore hard to see how such a system could have evolved. We must remember,

153

too, that some green algae are found at the greatest depths from which algae have been recorded.

Suppose that an alga happened to develop a red pigment in addition to chlorophyll. The red pigment would absorb blue-green light strongly, so that there would be less left over for the chlorophyll. Such a pigment would be a serious biological disadvantage, and would almost certainly be weeded out by natural selection *unless* the light it absorbed could be passed on to the chlorophyll for use in photosynthesis. If that were the case, it could be tolerated. It is quite possible that 'chromatic adaptation' arose in this way, rather than as a direct adaptation to assist photosynthesis.

We shall probably never know the truth of the argument, but we do know that light absorbed by accessory pigments can be passed on to chlorophyll *a* and used in photosynthesis. Whether the advantage gained by this determines the ability of an alga to survive remains open to question.

Although water is almost the universal hydrogen donor for photosynthesis in green plants, there are certain algae that can reduce carbon dioxide by means of elementary hydrogen. These include *Chlamydomonas moewusii*. It is said that a few can use hydrogen sulphide in place of water, including *Oscillatoria* (blue-green), *Scenedesmus* (green) and *Pinnularia* (a diatom). In this they resemble the sulphur bacteria.

Besides carbon dioxide for photosynthesis, algae, like all plants, need a variety of mineral substances, which they obtain from the surrounding water. In general they appear to need much the same elements as other plants. Usually the supply of minerals presents no problems, especially with marine algae, though nitrogen and, especially, phosphorus may limit the growth of the marine plankton at certain seasons.

For a long time marine biologists were puzzled at the curious seasonal periodicity shown by the numbers of microscopic plants that make up the phytoplankton. In spring, usually about March, these tiny creatures begin to multiply at an amazing rate, increasing their numbers sometimes ten-thousandfold in a fortnight. This is understandable, for spring is Nature's festival of reproduction, and an increase would be expected. As summer wears on, however, the numbers of phytoplankton decrease. Some, of course, are being eaten by larger members of the plankton, which have also increased in numbers, but the falling-off of the phytoplankton is much greater than could be accounted for in this way. By the late summer they have become relatively scarce. Then, when autumn is upon us, days are shortening and light is becoming feeble for photosynthesis, we suddenly find another increase in the phytoplankton; not as great as the spring increase, to be sure, but still considerable. When this new outburst is over the phytoplankton settles down again to its low winter level. This cycle is repeated year after year.

This strange sequence of events can be explained in terms of the available nitrogen and phosphorus, and especially of phosphorus. In the winter the waters of the oceans are well mixed and of nearly uniform temperature. When spring comes the phytoplankton passes into its reproductive phase, and there is a great increase in the phytoplankton in the upper layers of the water where it is light—remember that the phytoplankton is restricted to the upper or photic zone where there is light for photosynthesis. At the same time the water of the photic zone is heated by the increasing summer sun, the heated water floating on top of the colder layer beneath. Mixing of the upper layer with the water below is, for the time being, at an end. The creatures of the phytoplankton are using up nitrates and phosphates, which, as the organisms die and sink, are carried down to the bottom, out of reach. Soon there is not enough to go round, and the numbers of the phytoplankton fall as a consequence. Meanwhile, bacteria on the sea bottom are busy breaking down the organic detritus that is constantly falling, restoring nitrates and phosphates to the water. This does not help the phytoplankton, however, because the nutritive substances are locked away in the water below the photic zone, where they cannot penetrate, and the warm water floating on top prevents mixing.

As the summer passes into autumn, however, we have a

155

different set of conditions. The surface waters cool, and at the same time the gales of the autumn equinox churn up the water so that once again the nitrates and phosphates from below are carried up to the surface. When they reach the photic zone there is still light and warmth enough for the phytoplankton to take advantage of them, so that we get a fresh wave of reproduction before the winter, with its waning light, finally puts a stop to activity.

The actual amounts of nitrogen and phosphorus needed by algae are no larger than those required by other plants. *Pediastrum*, a fresh-water alga, needs 0·1 parts per million of nitrate of ammonia to make reasonable growth, and its growth increases up to a concentration of from 1 to 10 parts per million. At higher concentrations growth decreases again. Phosphorus is needed in smaller concentrations, from 0·01 to 0·1 parts per million being sufficient; with phosphorus there is no appreciable falling-off in growth when the concentration of phosphorus is increased to 100 parts per million.

Most of the algae that have been investigated seem to be fairly catholic in their taste as regards their nitrogen source, being able to use nitrates, ammonium salts and even some organic sources of nitrogen such as amino-acids. *Chlorella* prefers ammonium salts to nitrate, only absorbing nitrate after it has used up all the ammonium.

Phosphorus is normally taken in by algae in the form of phosphates, as it is in other plants, but in the laboratory it has been found that certain organic phosphorus sources, such as glycerophosphoric acid, phytin and an organic phosphate obtained from the fronds of *Laminaria*, can be absorbed. Other organic phosphorus compounds, such as lecithin and nucleinate, could not be used.

Besides nitrogen and phosphorus, iron is sometimes a limiting factor for the growth of algae. This is not because of any natural lack of iron in water, but because the iron is often present as insoluble compounds that algae cannot use. The growth of diatoms may also be limited by lack of silica, which they need for the construction of their frustules.

One can get some idea of the mineral needs of algae by burning them and then analysing the ash. These analyses show the same essential elements as higher plants, namely: nitrogen, phosphorus, sulphur, potassium, calcium, magnesium and iron, with smaller amounts of copper, boron, manganese and zinc. This by no means ends the list of elements that the algae absorb from sea water in minute quantities, however; an analysis of the ash of *Laminaria* has shown the presence of traces of silver, arsenic, cobalt, nickel, lead, tin, molybdenum, antimony, titanium, vanadium, tungsten, bismuth, gallium, germanium and gold. Whether these are 'casuals', or whether any of them are trace elements that are necessary to the life of the alga, we do not yet know. Higher plants now have an impressive list of elements—the trace elements—that are needed by the plants in the minutest quantities, and we can hardly doubt that the same applies to algae. In order to prove that an element is really essential, however, one has to prove that the plant will not grow properly without it, and this is by no means easy. So-called 'pure' chemicals, for instance, may contain minute traces of certain elements which defy chemical analysis, and yet which are enough to supply the needs of the plant. Even glass culture vessels are a rich source of some of the trace elements, which dissolve out of the glass into the culture solution that it contains. Specially refined research methods, therefore, must be used for work on the trace elements.

Many algae have an astonishing facility for accumulating potassium in their cells, apparently in the form of inorganic potassium salts. The kelps are a case in point; the great kelps such as *Macrocystis* and *Nereocystis* may have a concentration of potassium in their cells thirty times greater than in sea water. In some other algae the concentration is even higher. In *Valonia*, the large cells of which readily allow the cell sap to be extracted with a pipette and analysed, the concentration of potassium may be as great as fifty times its concentration in the water in which the plant is growing. Even *Valonia* is but a feeble concentrator, however, compared with certain algae growing in fresh or brackish water, such as *Nitella*, *Chara ceratophylla* and

Hydrodictyon. The cells of *Hydrodictyon* have been found on occasion to contain four thousand times as much potassium as the surrounding water.

Why these enormous concentrations of potassium should occur in certain algae is not known, nor do we know how the alga does it. To accumulate such quantities against the concentration gradient—that is, to transfer potassium from a place of low concentration (the water) to a place of higher concentration (the cell sap)—means that energy must be expended, so that some active metabolic forces must be operating.

Iodine is another element that is accumulated by certain algae; the former use of seaweeds as a source of iodine depended on this. *Laminaria* may accumulate iodine to the extent of 1 part per thousand of the whole plant, while the concentration of iodine in the sea water is only from 0·03 to 0·07 parts per million. In *Halicystis* (a green alga) the iodine in the cell sap may reach a concentration of ten thousand times that in sea water.

This accumulation of iodine is an even greater mystery than that of potassium, for we are not even sure of the form of the iodine in the plant. The general opinion is that it exists as simple iodide dissolved in the cell sap, though other views have been put forward.

Connected with the absorption of iodine is the phenomenon sometimes known as 'iodovolatization'. Everybody is familiar with the characteristic smell of the seashore, especially of the intertidal belt; it is popularly, but incorrectly, supposed to be due to ozone. In fact, it is the smell of iodine, given out by the seaweed that accumulates on the rocks. At one time it was thought that the smell came from iodoform, or some other organic compound of iodine, but it was noticed that in herbaria the paper on which certain seaweeds were mounted showed a blue stain, which was due to the action of iodine on starch in the paper. Tests showed that iodine could be detected by exposing paper impregnated with starch near to thalli of *Laminaria* that were left behind by the receding tide.

It still remains to be explained how iodides contained in seaweed give rise to free iodine in this way. It is thought that drying, exposure to strong light and other factors may damage the cells and allow the iodides to leak out, and that the iodides meet with oxidizing enzymes (organic catalysts) on the way out that release free iodine from them.

Various other substances, besides potassium and iodine, are sometimes accumulated by algae. Bromine accumulates in some marine algae, though not to the same extent as iodine; certain red algae can accumulate bromine up to about two hundred times its concentration in sea water. Chloride may also collect to some extent, but there is no evidence of any alga concentrating fluoride.

The algae are not alone in accumulating substances from the outside world, for there are many examples of higher plants which pick up and hoard the strangest things from the soil. The most extraordinary case of this that I know is a species of chickweed (*Holosteum umbellatum*), which appears to have a passion for mercury. When grown in soil that is rich in mercury salts it accumulates them to such an extent that droplets of metallic mercury appear in its cells. It is almost inconceivable that mercury in large quantities can be of any use to the plant, and the phenomenon can only be put down to some individual quirk in metabolism. Probably the accumulation of substances by algae must be ascribed to the same cause.

Alarm is sometimes expressed about the possibility that certain algae may be concentrating some of the poisonous fruit sprays and sheep dips that today are poisoning our countryside and gradually finding their way, via the rivers, to the sea. The idea of an alga which could accumulate a substance like fluoracetamide and pass it on, through the plankton food chain, to the herring is an awe-inspiring thought for anyone who likes to eat fish. Fortunately, however, such a thing is not at all likely. Algae can accumulate certain things like iodides that can enter their cells with ease and are not poisonous to the organism. Anything such as the relatively complex organometallic compounds used in sprays could scarcely enter the algal cells; if it did, and failed to kill the alga, the likelihood of its accumulating to dangerous proportions is not very great.

A greater danger exists in the 'fall-out' following a thermo-nuclear explosion, for there is a real possibility that this might be absorbed by algae of the phytoplankton and passed on, through fish, to man, through one of the many food chains that exist in the ocean. This needs further research.

Several harmful substances are released after an atomic 'test', the most dangerous of which is strontium-90. This is a metal very like calcium in its chemical properties, and wherever calcium is absorbed, strontium may be absorbed in its place. In the human body strontium-90 lodges in the bones, where most of the calcium is present, and in time it is liable to give rise to cancer. It has been calculated that for every atomic explosion of one megaton about a thousand people are likely to die of cancer during the next fifty years or so. Moreover, the bone sarcoma induced by strontium-90 is as liable to attack the young as the aged. It is a sobering thought that the 200-megaton Russian explosion in the Arctic Circle may have left two hundred thousand future cancer victims in its trail—more than the number killed at Hiroshima.

The chief danger from strontium-90 comes from drinking milk from cows grazed on grass affected by fall-out, for milk is the chief source of calcium, especially to babies. It is not, how-ever, the only source. It has been shown that plants take up strontium-90 in place of calcium, and there is no reason why the marine plankton should not do so. In this way it could be passed on to fish, and so to man.

Besides strontium-90, there are other by-products of an atomic explosion that are almost equally harmful, chief amongst which are radioactive caesium and radioactive iodine. From the algal point of view these may be even more dangerous. Caesium behaves like potassium, and may be taken into plants with potassium. In the animal body it concentrates in the muscles, and so may be eaten in meat—or fish. Algae that take in radio-active caesium are therefore a potential source of danger. The same could be said of iodine.

It may be that no danger really exists for the quantities of these substances passed on from algae to the animal world could

160

well be below the threshold necessary to cause harm. But we do not know, and until we do it is foolish in the extreme to imagine that fall-out is harmless as long as it falls into the ocean—whether the Arctic Ocean or the Pacific.

There is another danger also that needs watching. Atomic energy is being increasingly used for peaceful purposes, including the propulsion of ships. The time may come when radioactive substances from them may constitute a menace. Already the waters of the Holy Loch in Scotland, where the nuclear submarines are based, are radioactive, though we are officially assured that they are not sufficiently so to constitute a danger—yet. The danger, however, is there, if latent. One day it may cease to be latent, and by that time it will be too late to do anything about it except give up sea-bathing and eating fish for a hundred years or so.

Respiration in the algae seems in general to follow the normal pattern of other plants. They mostly get their energy by the oxidation of sugars by atmospheric oxygen, with the release of carbon dioxide. Research on various algae has shown the presence of the usual respiratory enzymes, and the complex cycle by which organic hydroxy-acids are converted one into another, known as the Krebs cycle, appears to proceed as in higher plants. Some algae show the phenomenon of oxidative assimilation, which means that part of the food material being respired is built back again into useful substances instead of being oxidized all the way to carbon dioxide and water. This is not uncommon in certain of the higher plants, so that here again the algae appear to be in no way abnormal.

An exception, however, must be made in certain of the Cyanophyta. In *Cylindrospermum*, for instance, respiration does not appear to follow the normal pattern, and more research is needed on the respiration on this and other species of Cyanophyta.

The occurrence of carbon monoxide in the flotation bladders of the giant kelp *Nereocystis* has puzzled physiologists. Carbon monoxide is the poisonous gas that occurs, amongst other places, in the exhaust fumes of motor cars. It is a respiratory

161

poison, even to plants, and yet in *Nereocystis* it seems to be a possible by-product of respiration. By what metabolic pathway it is produced is unknown. It is not found in the gas in the bladders of other algae, which contain only nitrogen, carbon dioxide and oxygen.

The question of whether some algae can or cannot fix atmospheric nitrogen has been debated for many years. Certain bacteria, such as *Azotobacter* and *Clostridium pasteurianum* in the soil, and *Rhizobium* in the root nodules of plants of the pea and bean family, undoubtedly have the power of fixing nitrogen from the atmosphere and so are independent of any other source. Whether certain algae also have that power has, until quite recently, been the subject of some controversy. Now, as described in Chapter 12, it has been established that at least some of the Cyanophyta can do it.

So far no complete proof exists that algae other than Cyanophyta can fix nitrogen, though there are signs that *Chlorella* may have the power to do so if grown under certain conditions.

It is interesting that *Nostoc* and its allies can only fix nitrogen if traces of molybdenum are present. In this they resemble the nitrogen-fixing bacteria. It may well be that the metabolic pathway to nitrogen fixation is much the same in the Cyanophyta and the bacteria.

The growth of higher plants is largely controlled by hormones, the best known of which is auxin (indolylacetic acid), which stimulates growth when it is present in certain concentrations. It is not surprising, therefore, to find evidence that growth hormones occur also in the algae. When the spores of *Ulva* and *Enteromorpha* have germinated, for instance, it is found that the young sporelings grow better if supplied with surface water that has been gathered from near other algae than if they are put into deep water that has not had algae growing in it. Apparently the other algae give out something that stimulates the growth of the sporelings. Auxin has actually been found in *Valonia*, as well as in a number of Pacific algae, including *Fucus evanescens* and *Macrocystis pyrifera*.

One of the effects of auxin in higher plants is to make possible

162

the existence of tropisms—the movements of part of a plant in response to outside stimuli acting in a certain direction. Examples are the growth of roots towards the force of gravity, and of stems away from gravity and towards light. When a plant stem, for instance, is illuminated from one side, auxin tends to accumulate on the side away from the light. As auxin stimulates the growth of stems, this has the result of making the stem grow faster on the dark side, so that it bends in the direction from which the light is coming. This phenomenon is known as phototropism. The same kind of thing has been observed in some of the algae.

Bryopsis, a green alga belonging to the Siphonales, has been the subject of considerable research on phototropism since it was shown as early as 1882 that it gave a marked phototropic response when illuminated from one side. The tips of the branches turn towards the light, while the rhizoids grow away from it. The response is particularly good with blue light, while red light produces no response at all—a point of similarity with phototropism in higher plants. *Bryopsis* was found to have a high auxin content, and it is difficult not to assume that the auxin is responsible for the phototropic responses, though it has not been proved.

I have already mentioned (Chapter 10) the remarkable polarity that develops in the fertile egg of *Fucus*, the end which comes into contact with the substratum becoming the base of the plant and cutting off a cell that forms the first rhizoid, while the other end grows out into the stipe and lamina of the new plant. This is sometimes called the 'group effect' because the rhizoid orientates itself towards the centre of the group if eggs occur in clumps, as they often do. Since the egg is originally spherical and shows no differentiation of one part from another, it seems clear that it must be some external stimulus which decides where the rhizoid is to be cut off, and where the stipe shall develop.

It is by no means certain how this 'group effect' works, but differences in the acidity or alkalinity of the surrounding water appear to play a part. A slight increase in the acidity of the water seems to favour the establishment of polarity, but larger increases in acidity inhibit it. Light also plays a part, probably through the influence of auxin, for *Fucus* is known to produce auxin in certain circumstances. Auxin applied directly to eggs, however, produces no effect.

Besides producing hormones that stimulate growth, some algae also form substances that inhibit growth. These growth inhibitors appear in cultures of algae when they have been grown for a long time without changing the water, and have the effect of slowly poisoning the culture. *Chlorella vulgaris* produces such an inhibitor, and an antibiotic called chlorellin has been extracted from *Chlorella* cultures, which yield from 0·01 to 0·02 grammes of chlorellin per litre of culture solution. Chlorellin is a crystalline substance which is not decomposed by heating to 120°C. From its chemical composition it would seem to be a mixture of organic acids known as fatty acids because some of them occur in fats. Chlorellin is active against *Staphylococcus aureus*, a common organism that causes infections of wounds, and various other bacteria, but it is not as potent as penicillin. The production of chlorellin seems to be one of the reasons why *Chlorella* is particularly useful in the purification of sewage effluents.

CHAPTER 14

Algae at home

The study of an organism in relation to its environment is called ecology. Compared with the wealth of information that has accumulated in recent years about the ecology of higher plants, algal ecology is still in its infancy. Yet in many respects a study of algal habitat relations should be a rewarding one, for they are, at least at times, abundant in a wide variety of places. In fresh water they grow in lakes, ponds, streams, and swamps—in fact, wherever there is fresh water, algae will almost certainly be there. They occur in soil, on tree-trunks, logs and palings, on rocks, on snow and ice, and, if this were not enough, algae are found in associations of various kinds with other plants and animals. In addition, algae are found in the seas of the world, from near the Poles to the Equator, and from the high tide mark down to depths of 600 feet. No other plants, if we except the bacteria, can grow in such a wide range of habitats.

Algae of fresh water

The algae of fresh water may be divided into groups or communities according to the type of place where they are found. First we have the plankton, or floating algae, which drift where the water currents will take them. Then we have the algae that grow attached to the mud or other material at the bottom of the water, algae growing in hot springs, algae that grow as epiphytes attached to other plants, and algae growing attached to aquatic animals. Each habitat has its own characteristic list of species, although in some cases the same algae may grow at different times in different situations.

165

The fresh-water plankton is composed largely of microscopic unicellular forms in which the diatoms are particularly conspicuous. To these may be added floating filamentous species, many of which have become detached from a fixed position by wave action or some other cause and so have joined the plankton.

Now and again the water of a pond or lake, or sometimes a slowly flowing river, becomes discoloured by a mass of floating plant life known as 'water-bloom'. Occasionally large areas of the sea may show a similar 'bloom'. In former days the development of a water-bloom was regarded as a warning of trouble to come. The earliest reference to water-bloom in Britain was the occurrence of red bloom at Finchhamsted, Berkshire, which was followed by the death of William Rufus in A.D. 1100. From time to time, however, much earlier examples of the water-bloom have been recorded in literature, the first example being in Exodus 7:19-21:

'. . . and all the waters that were in the river were turned to blood. And the fish that was in the river died and the Egyptians could not drink of the water of the river and there was blood in all the land of Egypt.'

Pliny, in A.D. 77, describes a lake in Babylon where the water turned red for eleven days in the summer, and also the Borysthenes (now known as the River Dnieper), which was blue in the summer.

A variety of algae can give rise to water-blooms under appropriate conditions. Some very fine examples are formed by the Cyanophyta, for many of them contain gas vacuoles which make them buoyant and able to accumulate at the surface of the water, especially if conditions are calm. Species of *Anabaena*, *Aphanizomenon*, and *Microcystis* are examples. Algae of other groups, however, may be responsible, and it has been recorded that at least sixty-five different species may form blooms. These include flagellates and diatoms. *Botryococcus braunii* may form green or brick-red specks in the surface waters of lakes, the colour depending upon conditions, and it has been shown that its buoyancy is due to the oil content of the cells. The 'boghead

166

coals' which are found in Scotland and also in Australia are derived almost entirely from the remains of plants which appear to be *Botryococcus*, or something very similar. These curious strata may well have been derived from *Botryococcus* blooms which occurred in carboniferous times.

Water-blooms at times have considerable economic importance, for they interfere both with water supplies and fishing, as well as with the work of fish farmers. Sometimes they may even poison cattle.

Some algae give both taste and smell to water, and so can cause trouble to water-supply organizations when they bloom; the problem may be intensified when they die, because decaying algae both taste and smell even worse than living ones. The matter does not rest there, for if algae in quantity were left in the water it would be too turbid to drink. The algae must therefore be removed from the water by filtration, and this can, on occasion, be a considerable problem.

Sometimes prophylactic measures may break down altogether. At the Ryton Water Works in Warwickshire, which supplies Coventry's water, there once occurred a phenomenal growth of the green flagellate *Euglena*. Besides discolouring the water, the algae passed through the filters and then managed to survive not only aluminium sulphate added to decolorize the water but also sterilization by chloramine. Attempts to treat the water for this nuisance failed completely, and it had to be pumped away.

Water-blooms can be as great a nuisance to the angler as to the water-supply authority. It is mainly blooms of blue-green algae that worry the fisherman, although other algae may also be a nuisance; the filamentous 'blanket weeds', such as *Spirogyra*, may be quoted as an example. Cyanophyta with gas vacuoles may float on or near the surface of the water and prevent the fish from seeing the lure. One of the worst blooms in angling history developed in the water of Loch Leven in 1937, reducing the catch of trout from the Loch to 23,538, compared with an average annual catch of 43,000. The alga that caused this trouble was *Oscillatoria borneti*, which produced more than

167

nine million filaments per litre of water at the time when it was most plentiful.

The indirect effect of blooms can also affect anglers adversely. In a small loch in Scotland, also in 1937, a bloom of the blue-green alga *Anabaena* developed suddenly. It so happened that, just when the bloom was at its peak, the temperature rose very quickly, thus producing particularly good conditions for the quick decomposition of the remains of the bloom. This sudden decomposition of vegetable matter caused an oxygen deficiency in the water, and, during a single night, no less than 640 trout died.

In many countries, especially in underdeveloped areas, fish farming is being revived as a means of producing extra food. Most of them exploit fish of the carp family which will make rapid growth as long as there is a copious supply of algae to supply food. The fish farmer adds fertilizers to the water of his pond in an attempt to encourage the growth of those species of algae which experience has taught him are specially valuable as fish food. Nobody, however, has yet invented a fertilizer which is specific in its action, so that the treatment encourages the blooming of blue-green algae, which forms a growth on the surface of the water that may discourage the development of the more useful algae both by reducing the light and by using up the available supply of nutriment. The development of a bloom in this way may even cause the death of a great many fish, for when the algae die their decomposition uses up oxygen, so that there is none for the fish to breathe.

Worse than the blooms caused by Cyanophyceae are those produced by a unicellular yellow-green alga called *Prymnesium parvum*, one of the Chrysophyceae. This produces a toxin which kills fish. *Prymnesium parvum* first came to notice as causing the death of fish in Holland and Denmark, but now it has invaded the Jordan Valley of Israel, the chief fish-farming area in the country. The control of *Prymnesium* became a matter of first importance, and it was soon discovered that the application of ammonium sulphate was usually effective in destroying it without hurting other algae. Since ammonium sulphate is in itself a fertilizer, this discovery was doubly welcome. Unfortunately it is not always effective.

Certain poisonous Cyanophyta are not only dangerous to fish, but may poison cattle, sheep and poultry. There are various records from America of domestic animals being poisoned in this way, and also it has been suggested that some cases of human gastroenteritis may have been caused by these algae.

Water-blooms, or similar phenomena, are not confined to fresh water. Periodically the water in parts of the North Sea take on a muddy appearance, known as 'baccy juice' by the fishermen. This is due to vast numbers of a coloured flagellate called *Phaeocystis ponchetii*. The organism is repulsive to herrings, and when, in the spring, *Phaeocystis* appears off the Dutch coast, the northbound herring migration is turned to the west, so that the herring fisheries of East Anglia benefit. Occasionally there may be an abnormal increase of *Phaeocystis* out of season, and when this occurs the southern migration of the herrings may be altered, with unpredictable result on the herring fisheries. This occurred in the year 1927.

One of the most severe marine water-blooms of modern times affected the coast of Florida. For a number of years they have been afflicted by a phenomenon known locally as the Red Tide: a reddening of the sea water by vast numbers of the dinoflagellate *Gymnodinium brevis*. This organism is pigmented— hence the red colour that it imparts to the water, which feels soapy to the touch. Fish that swim into the Red Tide are quickly killed, and their bodies are being washed up on the shores of Florida by the million, poisoned by the water-soluble toxin given off by the organism. Bulldozers have to be used to collect and dispose of the bodies of the fish. Even turtles and porpoises are killed. Sea birds and shore animals are poisoned by eating the fish, and shellfish are affected, so that it is dangerous to eat oysters or clams. The trouble reached a climax in the winter of 1962–3.

Apart from the danger of poisoning, the sea gives off a gas which, carried by the westerly wind, causes people on shore to cough and sneeze incessantly. The local citizens' committee is trying to get the State of Florida to sanction a grant of a quarter of a million dollars to finance a two-year research project to combat the pest, but they are being hampered by the 'chamber of commerce' mentality of a certain section of the community who feel that any publicity would interfere with the tourist trade.

The conditions that favour an outbreak of Red Tide seem to be heavy summer rains washing millions of tons of fresh water into the Gulf of Mexico, westerly winds holding this water near the shore, and fertilization of the water with phosphate carried down by rivers from phosphate mines in central Florida; when these conditions coincide there is usually trouble. More than five thousand chemicals have been tried by the Department of the Interior's Bureau of Commercial Fisheries to act as an algicide when poured into the rivers that feed the Gulf, but so far none has been found satisfactory.

The control of water-blooms is very important, especially in the protection of drinking water both for men and cattle, and a great deal of research has been undertaken on methods of killing the algae concerned, or at least limiting their growth.

For the treatment of water reservoirs coagulants are commonly used. These substances, in contact with water, produce large volumes of colloidal substances that entangle the algae and eventually sink to the bottom, carrying the algae with them. Alum is the coagulant that is most used; it reacts with water to produce a gelatinous mass of aluminium hydroxide. Coagulants are useful under the right conditions, but the production of suitable masses of aluminium hydroxide depends upon the hydrogen-ion concentration of the water, which may not always be suitable, and also requires special sedimentation tanks if its attack on the algae is to be fully successful.

Algicides are substances which kill algae directly, and are of more general use than coagulants. Their indiscriminate use, however, is not always successful. Although they may kill the unwanted algae, the decomposition of the dead plants may so enrich the water that it will soon support a further, bigger crop

170

of the algae it was sought to destroy. Copper sulphate is one of the best algicides to use, for it combines with nitrogenous compounds liberated by the algal cells to form insoluble substances, which sink to the bottom of the water and which are slow to decompose. Thus, the organic matter remains for some time beyond the reach of a further crop of algae, and being set free slowly, is unlikely to cause a bloom.

Where blooms occur annually, as they sometimes do, a knowledge of their periodicity may make it possible to kill the algae before they develop blooms. This is seen in Lake Monona, Wisconsin, where the algae are treated with the algicides before the bloom has grown to large proportions.

An objection to copper sulphate as an algicide is its permanent nature. When it has been used to kill algae, the compounds that the copper makes with the algal substance accumulate on the floor of the lake from year to year, and do not become harmless through the passage of time. If the lake is treated annually in this way it may build up a concentration of copper on its bottom that will, in time, have a serious effect on both the flora and the fauna. This has been found to be the case in certain lakes in America, and to avoid this effect attempts have been made to combat blooms with some of the organic weed-killers that are now on the market in such profusion. Recent experiments have shown that blooms of *Microcystis* and *Aphanizomenon* can be controlled with 2–3–dichloronaphthalene at twenty-five parts per thousand million. At this concentration, the poison has no effect, as far as can be made out, on any other form of life, but it is deadly to the algae.

The depth at which algae will grow depends on the amount of light available for photosynthesis. The light intensity is usually quite low for all submerged species, even those living at a depth of only a few inches, for the light-stopping power of water is considerable. In the deeper lakes on the continent of Europe the algae that grow deep down are often coloured red rather than green; another instance of chromatic adaptation. Algae, especially the algae that grow in deep water, usually have a low compensation-point: that is, the intensity of light where

171

respiration and photosynthesis just balance one another has a lower value than in most plants that grow on land.

On the rocky bottoms of shallow water we often find incrustations of diatoms, and certain blue-green algae also favour this habitat.

The algal population of streams varies according to the speed of the water current, which may be anything from a gently meandering lowland brook to a mountain torrent. In rapidly flowing water the algal population is largely composed of freshwater red algae, such as *Lemanea* and *Compsopogon*, with *Batrachospermum* in more acid water, and such green algae as *Cladophora*, together with diatoms, various Chrysophyceae and Cyanophyceae. Where the water moves more slowly the *Cladophora* tends to give way to *Enteromorpha* and *Hydrodictyon*; in a very sluggish stream, as well as in lakes, floating mats of *Enteromorpha*, *Hydrodictyon*, *Spirogyra* and *Oedogonium* are not uncommon. In the United States particularly, almost pure stands of *Hydrodictyon reticulatum* may be encountered in sluggish water.

The algal flora of ponds and ditches varies according to a number of factors, and there is often a periodicity, certain types being dominant at certain times. In temperate regions the chief algae of ponds and ditches are various Protococcales, with Zygnemaceae such as *Spirogyra* and *Zygnema* dominant in the spring and diatoms dominant in the winter. The larger filamentous forms such as *Cladophora* seldom appear, probably because the aeration of the water is not high enough for them. In fact, we can divide ponds and ditches into those containing Cladophoraceae, where presumably the aeration happens to be particularly good, and those without.

In a tropical pond the algal flora is different from that of a pond in temperate regions. There are usually plenty of Cyanophyceae present, and an abundance of desmids and *Spirogyra*.

In determining the algal flora of lakes the geology of the lake bottom appears to be very important. Where the lake is formed in old rock—older than the Carboniferous period—you tend to get a rich desmid flora, while in younger rocks the diatoms become more common. The first is said to be oligotrophic water, while the second is called eutrophic water. There is also a type known as dystrophic water, found on moorlands, which is highly coloured, and here the desmids form the major part of the flora.

At one time there was supposed to be a sharp distinction between the nature of oligotrophic, eutrophic and dystrophic waters, but we now realize that the distinction is less absolute, for one type may change with time into another.

In bogs and swamps, where conditions are, on the whole, very uniform, we find that algal associations are very mixed. The most frequent algae are Zygnemaceae, diatoms and desmids. Desmids in particular are very variable, and change according to the altitude of the bog.

The algae that inhabit hot springs are particularly interesting, and have attracted a great many workers. The Cyanophyceae play a major part and are often the only algae that are present. Generally speaking, plant and animal cells cannot live in a temperature above 50°C, exposure to temperatures higher than this killing them more or less quickly. The blue-green algae, with the bacteria, are exceptions, and commonly inhabit the waters of hot springs at very much higher temperatures.

In hot springs in the Yellowstone National Park, Copeland found blue-green algae growing, apparently quite happily, at temperatures up to 85°C. He found the greatest number of species growing within the range of 30°C to 35°C, although there were almost equally many growing at from 35° to 40°C. The highest recorded temperature for water containing living plants is 87·5°C, a temperature which *Phormidium luminosum* seemed quite easily able to survive. Altogether, the springs at Yellowstone Park yielded 53 genera and 153 species. Most of them belonged to the families Chroococcaceae and Oscillatoriaceae. Broadly speaking, they can be divided into three types: those found only in thermal waters; those characteristic of a wide variety of habitats (facultative thermophytes); and algae really characteristic of cooler waters which have successfully invaded

173

the hot-water habitat. The first two groups seem to be composed entirely of Cyanophyceae, while the third group includes certain other algae, especially diatoms, and even some animals.

Nobody has explained why the Cyanophyceae should be able to grow at higher temperatures than most other organisms, though various suggestions have been made. There may be something about the peculiar structure of their protoplasm, or their primitive organization without definitive nuclei, or they may be vestiges of the flora that inhabited the earth a long time ago, when temperatures were very much higher than they are now. It is also possible, though not very likely, that the rates of physiological processes in the blue-green algae are less affected by temperature than those of other plants.

Under the general heading of halophytes we include algae that have been found in salt lakes and springs with a salt content varying from two to seventeen times that of the sea. The algae inhabiting such salt water are mostly Chlorophyta, though numbers of other groups, especially Cyanophyta, Euglenophyta and diatoms occur. *Dunaliella* and *Stephanoptera* have been found in the area of Searle's Lake, California, forming a green growth on crusts of solid salt where the water contains 33 per cent of dissolved solids.

Some algae are found in even stranger places, such as water polluted by acid mine wastes with a high concentration of sulphuric acid. Twenty-four species of algae were found in streams or ponds of the coal-mining regions in West Virginia, Illinois and Indiana, where the range of pH varied from 1·8 to 3·9. The species included *Euglena mutabilis*, *Chromulina ovalis*, a species of *Ochromonas*, *Ulothrix zonata*, and various diatoms. A number of Cyanophyta are also to be found growing in the film of water on the surface of pools and ditches which contain crude oil.

The number of algae found as epiphytes on other plants, and occasionally animals, in fresh water is very large, and it is difficult to assess acurately, because many are there, as it were, accidentally. A germinating zoöspore may happen to lodge on the stem of an aquatic plant and germinate there, and the alga

174

that grows from it may become attached, either temporarily or permanently, although normally it is not an epiphyte. Moreover, it is a little artificial to separate those algae that commonly grow attached to plants from those growing on submerged inorganic material such as stones. In any case, an epiphyte may grow on dead as well as living parts of the host plant, and even on living portions it is dubious, to say the least, whether the surface that the alga is growing on is necessarily to be considered 'alive'; the external part of the epidermal cell wall, for instance, could probably be dead as far as the alga is concerned.

On the other hand, certain algae seem to occur with more or less regularity as epiphytes, both on other algae and on higher plants. One could mention *Tribonema* and *Tetraspora* on various plants in the early spring; *Rivularia* on various rushes in summer; *Bulbochaete*, *Oedogonium* and diatoms on culms of sedges, rushes and grasses, and many others. Floating leaves are found to have different epiphytes on the lower surface compared with the upper surface. Some algae, and especially diatoms, are found more often on the older parts of the hosts, while other algae are more common on younger parts. It is generally true that parts of the host which grow slowly carry more epiphytes than those which grow quickly.

Most large filamentous algae are hosts for a number of epiphytes, though some of the Zygnemateles are exceptions on account of the solubility of the pectic compounds which compose the outer layer of their cell walls, which gives them a slimy coating which resists the lodgement of spores from other algae. Even mobile forms may have their epiphytes, for a species of *Euglena* has been found growing on *Volvox*.

Marine algae

The algae that inhabit the sea have been much studied, especially those species which are found on rocky shores, and a great deal of information has been obtained about them. In studying the ecology of marine algae, and especially the larger forms, one is immediately struck by the fact that certain ecological factors which are of life-and-death importance to land plants have little meaning in the sea. Rainfall, for instance, and humidity, are without meaning for submerged algae. Temperature is much less variable in the sea than on land, and the constant composition of sea water is very unlike the variability found in the soil. On the other hand, certain special factors are present in the sea and not on land. The constant disturbance of the water by wave action, and the periods of emersion of littoral species owing to the action of the tides, have no counterpart on land.

In considering first of all the factors that act on marine benthic algae—that is, algae that grow attached to the substratum—we find that the chemical nature of the substratum appears to have no great significance. The substratum only serves as a place for attachment of the holdfast; the algae take in nothing from it, getting all the food elements from the water of the sea. This is in sharp contrast to a land plant, which gets all its essential elements, except carbon, from the soil through its roots. The physical nature of the substratum, however, is important, because of its effect on the attachment of the alga, and it is not surprising that marine algae show preferences for one type of substratum or another; solid rock, gravel, sand, mud, etc.

Although the temperature of sea water is very much less variable than the temperature on land, annual variation in the surface temperature of the sea may be quite considerable. In tropical seas, it is true, the annual variation may be only 2° to 3°C, but along the Atlantic coast of South America it often exceeds 18°C. This variability, of course, extends only to the surface waters; as you go deeper so the variation in temperature becomes less, until finally the temperature becomes practically constant. Thermal variation is much greater in coastal regions than in the open sea. Thermal variation can cause a seasonal migration of algae to different levels according to the temperature of the water at the time.

The intensity of illumination has a profound effect on the development of algae. As light penetrates into water, the longer wavelengths—red, orange and yellow—are absorbed more

176

quickly than the blue and violet. This means that the deeper we go, the more light changes in colour. Light not only changes in colour, of course; it also grows dimmer, and at last a point will be reached where the intensity of the light is no longer sufficient to support a photosynthetic organism. Beyond this point the algae cannot grow. The depth at which lack of light limits the occurrence of algae varies; in northern waters we do not find algae at greater depths than about 200 feet, but in warmer seas, where the water often has less sediment held in suspension and therefore passes light better, algae can grow much deeper. At Dry Tortugas, in Florida, algae have been collected at a depth of over 300 feet, and in the very clear water of the Mediterranean they grow even deeper. In the Gulf of Naples they grow down to 400 feet, and in the Balearic Islands they have been found to a depth of over 500 feet. The maximum depth at which algae are able to live seems to be approximately 600 feet, though they very seldom attain this depth.

I have already spoken of the chromatic adaptation that exists amongst algae, the red algae being particularly adapted to use light of short wavelength and low intensity for photosynthesis. Although this chromatic adaptation exists, however, it is not absolute, for we find green algae adapted to live at great depths and red algae which occur in full sunlight.

Another effect of deep water is pressure. The deeper one goes, the greater the pressure of the water above. We have all heard of divers who suffer from the condition known as 'the bends' if they come up too quickly from a great depth; under the effect of external pressure nitrogen is forced into their blood, and if the pressure is relaxed too suddenly it bubbles out again, producing severe cramps. Pressure does not seem to have any effect on benthic algae excepting the species with gas-filled bladders, which cannot grow in deep water. In many species the thickness of the bladder wall varies with the depth at which the alga is growing, and if an individual is suddenly taken to a lower level it loses the gas in its bladders and may die.

The salinity of sea water varies very little from one part of the world to another, though it is higher in the tropical seas than in the oceans of the colder parts of the world. The average salinity is in the neighbourhood of 35 grammes per litre, of which the major part is sodium chloride, but in the Red Sea it reaches over 40 grammes per litre.

These relatively small variations in salinity do not seem to affect benthic algae very much, though they have considerable effect on planktonic algae because they affect buoyancy. Where the salinity is affected by the mouth of a river, however, we may find that certain benthic species disappear and that others take their place. At the other end of the scale, in rock pools, lagoons and other places where sea water becomes isolated, the evaporation of water may cause the salinity to rise very much, so that the growth of many species is prevented. Some algae, such as species of *Enteromorpha*, have a wide range of salinity in which they can grow, and for them the best salinity for growth may not be that of sea water. *E. intestinalis* makes its best development in slightly diluted sea water, though it can grow in fresh water, brackish water, sea water, or even in a brine solution.

The pH of sea water is slightly on the alkaline side, being usually between 7·9 and 8·3 (most commonly 8·1 to 8·2). This is because most of the carbon dioxide it contains is in the form of carbonates and bicarbonates. The photosynthetic activities of algae, which remove carbon dioxide from the water, cause bicarbonates to dissociate as they do so, and this means that the water becomes more alkaline. In rock pools containing green algae, especially *Ulva*, which is very active photosynthetically, the pH may rise as high as 10 as a result of exposure to light for a few hours, and many algae cannot stand water as alkaline as this. It is noticeable that the presence of *Ulva* in a rock pool in any quantity often means the elimination of certain other species, particularly many red algae.

The effect of wave action on algae is very obvious if we compare the algal flora of a headland with that in a bay. The one is fully exposed to waves while the other is protected so that the water is less disturbed. The effect of waves on the algal population is rather complex. On the one hand, on the headland the waves may prevent the fixation of spores to the rocks, or tear loose the more fragile algae that grow from spores that have managed to find a lodgement. It must not be supposed, however, that algae will necessarily grow better in less turbulent water, for relatively calm water may allow a deposit of mud to be formed on the rocks; this will prove a bar to the development of some algae, though others may be favoured by it.

The effect of tides on the algal population is profound. On any rocky coast you can see the phenomenon of zonation: some species grow high up on the shore, while others prefer a situation lower down and nearer the sea. This zonation is found all over the world, and does not necessarily depend upon a large tidal rise; it can be clearly seen in parts of the Caribbean where the mean tidal rise is only about 9 inches. Zonation is, however, most easily seen on a gently sloping shore and where the tidal rise and fall is fairly great.

Zonation is never shown better than on the colder Atlantic shores of Europe. The highest zone, known as the supra-littoral fringe, is inhabited by *Porphyra umbilicalis* and *Pelvetia canaliculata*. This belt is above the normal range of high tides and it is covered only by the highest of spring tides. Next we have a belt of *Fucus spiralis*, and below that a belt of *Asco-phyllum nodosum*, followed by one of *Fucus vesiculosus*; the position of these two may be reversed, and there is usually a middle belt where both species occur. Below these again we find *Fucus serratus*, and, finally, in the sublittoral fringe, which is immersed all the time, we find species of *Laminaria*, particularly *L. digitata*.

A determining factor in the establishment of these belts seems to be the period during which the plants are emersed. Algae such as *Pelvetia canaliculata* and *Fucus spiralis* can stand long periods of emersion; in fact, it has been found by experiment that they die quite quickly if they are kept constantly sub-merged. *Fucus serratus*, on the other hand, cannot withstand being emersed for long, so it grows in the lower littoral zone, near the sea, where it is covered for at least 50 per cent of the time.

Another effect that the rhythm of the tides has upon certain

179

benthic algae is to implant a periodicity on the emission of their reproductive cells. We have already seen this is so in *Dictyota dichotoma*, and the phenomenon has also been noticed in other marine algae, including species of *Ulva* from the Monterey Peninsula, which fruits at fortnightly intervals, the fruiting corresponding with spring tides.

Although the large benthic algae catch our eye as the most obvious marine plant life, we must not forget that the seas contain vast numbers of smaller forms. The phytoplankton, as the microscopic floating species are called, plays an important part in the bionomics of the ocean. These little organisms, invisible to the naked eye, are found everywhere, from the Equator to Arctic and Antarctic regions. Although they are individually so small, they make up in numbers what they lack in size; if the plankton of the oceans could be weighed, it would be found to outweigh all other forms of plant life.

The phytoplankton of the sea is of immeasurable biological significance, because it forms the ultimate food of everything that lives in the ocean. Some fishes feed directly on it, straining the tiny organisms out of the sea water that they swallow, but most of them feed on smaller animals that have themselves fed on plankton. In this way are made up innumerable 'food chains', starting with phytoplankton, passing through sometimes several intermediate stages and ending up as fish.

The phytoplankton consists largely of diatoms and dinoflagellates, but also includes certain Cyanophyta and Chlorophyta. The dinoflagellates are a mixed group, some of which are photosynthetic and may be regarded as true algae, while the rest have no chlorophyll and are animal-like. The diatoms we have already met; most of the marine phytoplanktonic forms are centric, pennate forms being more characteristic of fresh water.

The usual method of collecting phytoplankton is to draw a fine net, called a plankton net, through the water; at the base of the net is a tube in which most of the planktonic organisms collect. Not all plankton, however, can be collected in this way, for some forms, including the smaller diatoms and dinoflagellates, are too small to be caught by the mesh of even the finest net; such forms are sometimes called nannoplankton (*nanus*— a dwarf). Amongst the nannoplankton are many chlorophyll-containing organisms, and although they have not been studied to the same extent as the larger plankton, there is little doubt that their importance in the economy of the ocean is very great.

A plankton net only collects from 1 to 10 per cent of the phytoplankton in a sample of water. If a more complete sample is required, the plankton cells can be removed from the water by centrifuging, by allowing the water to stand so that the cells settle down, or by filtering through a membrane filter.

The amount of carbon produced by photosynthesis by the marine plankton is surprisingly large. Various measurements give the figures varying between 44 and 1,000 grammes of carbon per square metre of sea every year. The lower figures tend to be from very shallow waters where photosynthesis does not extend far in depth, while the higher figures are for areas of considerable depth where the photosynthetic zone extends down until cut off by lack of illumination. Relatively high values are also obtained in places where the concentration of nutritive substances in the surface layers is increased by the mixing of water by currents.

There seems to be no great difference in carbon production between tropical waters and the waters of higher latitudes. It is true that the concentration of plankton near the surface is higher in colder latitudes, but in the tropics the greater depth of the photosynthetic zone makes up for the drop in concentration. It has been estimated that the oceans of the world, by their photosynthetic activity, produce between 44×10^9 and 208×10^9 tons of carbon per year, while the total world photosynthesis, land and ocean combined, is between 59×10^9 and 233×10^9 tons. From these figures it will be seen that the contribution of the oceans greatly exceeds the contribution of the land, and a considerable portion of this oceanic contribution must be put down to the phytoplankton.

The annual production of organic carbon by phytoplankton in the sea has been calculated to lie between 0·52 and 10·35 tons of dry plankton per acre per year, with an average value of about 3·2 tons per acre per year. These figures can stand comparison with most land crops. A corn crop averages about 6·6 tons per acre fresh weight, with a grain yield of 2·36 tons. Oats give a value of about half a ton fresh weight, and at the other end of the scale sugar beet gives about 13 tons fresh weight. It must be remembered that these are *fresh weight* figures, and would be reduced by a considerable amount if their water content were deducted.

Soil algae

It is difficult, if not impossible, to draw a hard-and-fast line between fresh-water and soil algae, for in the soil the particles are covered with a minute film of moisture in which the algae live. Many species found in the soil are fresh water species which have made the soil their habitat either temporarily or permanently, and many 'soil' algae are perfectly at home in fresh water. In fact, phycologists have not yet fully decided whether a separate algal flora of the soil exists, or whether soil algae are merely forms putting up with soil as a habitat when they would rather be in fresh water.

The enumeration of soil algae is not altogether easy, first because the plants themselves are often very small, and secondly because it frequently happens that only spores are present, and these are not easy to see when examining the soil. It is therefore necessary when studying soil algae to 'plant' or inoculate soil on to an artificial medium in order to encourage the algae present to grow out of the soil and be recognized. Such cultures usually do not give a complete picture of all the algae that are present, and they are not much use to the ecologist except in as much as they show approximately what algae are present.

On the whole, it seems to be generally recognized now that the soil has its definite algal flora, even if some of the species are also found in water. Some species, however, have been recorded only from soils; amongst these are species of *Botrydium, Protosiphon, Zygnema, Zygogonium, Oedogonium,*

Botrydiopsis, Vaucharia and *Microcoleus*. In some soils algae are very abundant, an ounce of soil containing something like a million of them. Well-manured soil usually has a particularly rich flora, and the numbers of algae present are also affected by the soil moisture, more algae being present in damp than in dry soil. Diatoms in particular are much more abundant when the soil is rich in phosphates and nitrates, while more acid types of soil are usually poor in diatoms. There is a seasonal aspect affecting the number of algae in the soil, but their behaviour depends very much on the depth and nature of the soil, which makes it difficult to separate the effect of season from the effects of other factors.

Algae occur both on the surface of the soil and buried to a depth of, sometimes, several feet. Since they require light for photosynthesis, it is natural that they should occur in greatest numbers near the soil surface, but they can be found at a surprising depth. Soil-culture work has shown that algae are mainly confined to the top 12 inches of the soil, but algae have been recovered from soil in Greenland to a depth of 40 centimetres. Those found in the depths presumably came originally from the surface, and have been carried down by the action of burrowing animals, or, as in the Greenland examples, by water trickling down cracks in the soil.

How algae manage to exist deep in the soil where they are cut off from sunlight is still a mystery. They clearly cannot photosynthesize, and so, assuming that they exist in an active state, they must nourish themselves saprophytically. What seems more likely, however, is that they are present in the form of spores or other 'resting' bodies, which can remain dormant for long periods, only bursting into life again when they are exposed to favourable conditions, including the presence of light.

In addition to the algae of the soil, there are various terrestrial species to be found growing as epiphytes on leaves and bark, as well as those species that are found on rocks, palings, and even on land animals. These species are sometimes called aerophytes.

ALGAE AT HOME

One finds far more true epiphytes in tropical regions than in temperate areas, just as with the higher plants, and, conversely, in districts where the winters are long and severe the number of epiphytes is correspondingly reduced. Some, probably most, epiphytic algae merely use their host plant as something to grow on, never penetrating below the surface. Others, however, may grow beneath the surface of the epidermis of the host, and must be considered partly or largely parasitic. The very widespread *Cephaleuros* is often found in tropical and subtropical parts, growing on many hosts, including orange, lemon, grapefruit and tea.

Many algae inhabit bark, and are known as epiphloeophytes. Many of them are associated with mosses. *Phormidium* and *Scytonema* amongst the Cyanophyta, and *Trentepohlia* and *Prasiola* among the Chlorophyta, are examples, but the best known epiphloeophyte in the north temperate zone is *Pleurococcus*, which is almost ubiquitous, growing on the trunks of trees up to a height of about 30 feet from the ground.

Algae which grow on the surfaces of stones and rocks are known as lithophytes. Their habitat varies from the extreme hardness of granite to the comparative softness of sandstone, and from full sunshine to shade; they may be wetted most of the time by trickling water, or exposed to extreme desiccation, often accompanied by the most intense heat. On exposed rocks the Cyanophyta are particularly conspicuous, including *Gleocapsa, Rivularia, Stigonema* and others, while on more shady cliffs with a damp surface we may find, amongst others, *Trentepohlia, Prasiola* and *Vaucheria*, as well as some Cyanophyta, diatoms and others. Lichens, of course, abound on certain rock surfaces.

Many algae enter into symbioses of various kinds with both other plants and animals. The most important of these is the association between the algae and fungi, forming lichens, already dealt with. *Anabaena* enters into various associations with higher plants, including its growth within the tiny water-fern *Azolla*, and in the apogeotropic roots of cycads; *Nostoc* and other Cyanophyta are to be found in *Anthoceros*, cycads and certain

184

flowering plants. A strange instance of close relationship between two plants is found in the alga, probably related to *Oocystis*, whose 'chloroplasts' are really unicellular blue-green algae. In many cases the alga probably contributes little or nothing to the well-being of the host, and should perhaps be regarded as a 'space-parasite', but in others it seems fairly certain that the alga is able to fix atmospheric nitrogen, making it available to the host in exchange for some other food material such as sugar or protein. This seems to be the case, for instance, with *Anabaena* and *Cycas*.

There are various instances of associations between the algae and animals, among which the green algae known as zoochlorellae in *Hydra* and *Convoluta* are examples which have already been described. A curious instance of algae living on an animal is seen in *Cyanoderma* and *Trichophylus*, which live on the hair of the sloth, giving the animal a greenish colour. These might perhaps be compared with epiphloeophytes on bark.

Certain species of algae inhabit the respiratory and digestive tracts of vertebrate animals. *Simonsiella*, for instance, has been isolated, not only from man, but from the horse, cow, pig, goat, sheep and fowl. How these algae get there we do not know; possibly they originate on food, and they may be only temporarily inhabiting the digestive or respiratory tracts, although once there they remain attached for some time, so that they may be described as a 'flora'. Living in total darkness, they must be either parasitic or saprophytic, though they may regain the power of photosynthesis when they are exposed to light.

CHAPTER 15

The uses of algae

A student of mine, set to write an essay on 'Algae and their importance', began, after some thought, 'Most algae are something of a nuisance.' I do not know what was at the back of his mind when he wrote this; perhaps he was a fisherman thinking of water-blooms, or it may have been an expression of his opinion of lecturers who gave him impossible subjects to write on. At any rate, it was a gross libel. A few algae make nuisances of themselves on occasion, as anyone who has smelt the decaying seaweed at Worthing on a summer day will agree; in the main, they are among the most harmless plants in the world, and some are very useful indeed.

The earliest use of seaweeds was probably as food for man and beast. We do not know when they were first eaten, but the first phycophages, if I may coin a word, may well have lived in caves near the coast and wandered abroad clad in skins with perhaps a touch of woad here and there. The eating of seaweed has persisted to the present day, especially in China, Japan and Hawaii. The ancient Polynesians, whose villages were generally situated near the sea, used to cultivate sea 'gardens' where various edible seaweeds were kept in culture. The same habit is found in Japan, where today *Porphyra* is extensively cultivated for eating. The *Porphyra* 'farmers' stick bamboo poles into shallow water, usually in bays and the mouths of rivers, each 'farm' measuring about 120 feet × 7 feet. The bamboo becomes covered with the sporelings of *Porphyra*, and when they are judged to bear sufficient they are pulled up and replanted, usually in an estuary where the water is less saline than in the open sea. The *Porphyra* continues to grow on the bamboo and is eventually harvested. Nowadays the bamboo sticks are often replaced by nets.

Besides growing *Porphyra*, the Japanese have an algal food called kombu, which is made from the large oarweeds such as *Laminaria*, *Alaria*, *Arthrothamnus* and others. The weed is gathered from the sea, the fishermen using open boats and specially designed hooks. It is then dried and cut up in different ways, so that you can have a choice of black or white pulpy kombu, shredded kombu, filmy kombu, hair kombu, or sweet-cake kombu. The quantity of weed gathered in this way is enormous; in 1936 it was nearly 300,000 tons wet weight.

Various other Japanese foods are prepared from seaweeds, including arame, which comes from *Eisenia bicyclis*, hijiki from *Hijikia fusiforme*, miru from *Codium*, wakame from *Underia pinnatifida*, and many others. Hawaii is not one whit behind Japan in eating seaweeds, for over forty species are used, most of them being green or red algae.

In the Western world little use is made of seaweed itself for eating, though extracts have been extensively used. *Porphyra* is still used for making laver bread, and the Irish moss (*Chondrus crispus*) retains its devotees. On the whole, however, we are not adventurous when it comes to phycophagy.

There is some doubt about the nutritional value of edible seaweeds. Probably they supply mainly carbohydrates, though the Japanese *Porphyra* and edible Chinese *Nostoc* have been found to have a high nitrogen content. It would seem that eating algae is of more benefit to people in poor health, and probably their main value is in providing roughage in the diet, especially in places like Japan where the food of many people consists largely of rice and fish.

Apart from their actual nutritional value seaweeds may be of use on account of the iodine that they contain. Many seaweeds have an almost uncanny knack of retaining iodine from sea water, so that the thalli contain a relatively high proportion of this element. It is found that in countries where people use seaweed regularly as a food goitre scarcely appears at all; as is well known, goitre is a condition brought on primarily by lack of iodine in the diet.

I have already mentioned the use of seaweeds, especially the brown seaweeds, as fodder for animals. In the poorer parts of northern Europe, in particular, they are quite extensively used to feed animals, being particularly valuable for their vitamins and their trace elements. Farther south, seaweed meal is often used to make up a balanced ration for feeding to cattle, pigs and poultry. Seaweeds appear to be rather more digestible to animals than they are to human beings, and, apart from their use as food, they seem to have a generally good effect on the condition of the beasts; this is probably due to the presence of vitamins and trace elements.

There is another aspect of algae as food which has recently gained some notoriety, and which may well play a vital part in the nourishment of people in underdeveloped countries in the future. This is the development of the unicellular alga *Chlorella* as a human food by growing it in bulk. The idea has distinct possibilities. If we measure the efficiency with which an ordinary crop uses light energy in the production of organic matter by photosynthesis, we find that it is usually less than 1 per cent— that is, less than 1 per cent of the energy in the sunlight falling on the area occupied by the crop is converted into potential chemical energy in carbohydrates. If this efficiency could be increased it would be possible to get much greater yields per unit area of the earth's surface. It has been calculated that the maximum energy with which a plant could convert the energy of sunlight into carbohydrate is about 30 per cent, but for various reasons such a rate of conversion is beyond practical attainment. With *Chlorella*, and algae like it, a much higher efficiency of conversion can be attained, and it is possible so to influence the metabolism of *Chlorella* growing in culture so that a high proportion of useful as compared with useless matter can be accumulated.

It was the Second World War which gave the necessary stimulus to research on the mass cultivation of *Chlorella*, and work was started both in Germany and America. The American work has been continued since the war, and scientists in Britain also have been busy. They have shown that it is quite possible to attain a high photosynthetic efficiency in a mass culture of *Chlorella*, and that the result is a product containing a great deal of high-grade protein which is perfectly satisfactory as a food. Experiments on feeding it to rats have shown that it produces no ill effects. Unfortunately, the capital required to set up the necessary plant to cultivate *Chlorella* on a large scale is at present prohibitive. It does not seem likely at the moment that *Chlorella* farms will ever replace the more conventional type, and heaven forbid that they should; but it does seem possible that the method will ultimately be used in producing human food in arid areas, where edible protein produced by other methods is extremely scarce. One cannot, however, foresee the future, and it is always dangerous to make prophecies in matters of this kind. Possibly someone will discover that *Chlorella* produces an antibiotic of unprecedented importance, or that some other by-product of this little alga has a high commercial value as yet unsuspected. If this should happen, we may end up by eating *Chlorella* whether we like it or not.

The use of algae for the treatment of sewage has recently come into prominence, especially in America. Sewage used to be regarded as a waste material to be got rid of with as little fuss as possible, but today it is being looked upon more and more as a potentially valuable raw material. Sewage contains nitrogen, phosphates and potash, the three things that are most in demand in building up the fertility of the land. It has been estimated that the nitrogen discharged in sewage effluents in Great Britain contains about one-third of the country's needs in nitrogenous fertilizers, and at present nearly all this valuable element is being wasted. Some sewage works are now recovering a great deal of the valuable organic matter in the sludge for use as a manure for the land, but a great deal remains to be done. Also, even where the reclamation of sewage sludge is carried out, much of the nitrogen, phosphates and potash remain in solution in the effluents that are allowed to go to waste after the treatment has been given.

189

The biological treatment of sewage is essentially a process of oxidation, the organic matter being broken down by bacteria, using atmospheric oxygen. The oxygen required for the process is supplied mechanically, either by spraying the sewage into the air and allowing it to fall on to beds of stones or coke, or by blowing air into it; sometimes the sewage is kept in motion by means of moving paddles. Such processes are expensive both to lay out and to run.

There is, however, another way of providing the oxygen that is needed without costly mechanical plant and maintenance. Algae, growing in the water in which the organic matter is suspended, will supply all the oxygen that is needed as a by-product of their photosynthesis, and at the same time they will absorb into their bodies much of the soluble nitrogen, phosphorus and potash that would otherwise run to waste. When the process of biological oxidation is completed the algae can be harvested; they can then be eaten by man, fed to animals or used as a manure for the land.

This is the principle behind the sewage oxidation ponds. The sewage is allowed to run into a shallow lagoon. Species of microscopic algae, especially *Chlorella* and *Scenedesmus*, growing in the sewage, supply the oxygen that is needed by the hordes of bacteria that break down the organic matter in the sewage, at the same time destroying harmful substances and making the residual liquid safe for disposal. Under favourable conditions as much as 2 grammes dry weight of algae can be grown per litre of liquid; multiplied by the millions of gallons passing through the sewage farm, this comes to quite a respectable total.

The process is not without its snags, however, and there is still much work to be done before the produce of the sewage farm will put the orthodox farmer out of business. For one thing, the space occupied by the large, shallow lagoons that are needed for the process is considerable, and also the weather is an important factor, for algae need sunlight for photosynthesis. This is why the initial experiments have been made in California, where there are open spaces to spare and the sunny climate is ideal. Whether the process would be an economic proposition in England is dubious on both counts, though work that is going on at present on the enrichment of the algal flora of the lagoons may bear interesting fruit if it comes to initiating the process in these islands, where space is at a premium and the climate gets ever more gloomy. It is in the underdeveloped parts of the world, however, that the algal treatment of sewage holds out most promise; with unlimited space and constant sunshine, the possibilities are almost unlimited.

The harvesting of the algae presents a considerable problem, for centrifuging, the standard laboratory process of separating small algae from water, would cost far too much. Coagulation with aluminium sulphate, the method used for dealing with 'water-blooms', would be too costly for an underdeveloped country where the aluminium sulphate would have to be imported, and there would still be the problem of separating the algae from the colloidal aluminium salt in the end product. It has been found that some blue-green algae aggregate together during growth, so that eventually they may be separated by sedimentation; perhaps in the future this may be the answer.

The cultivation of microscopic algae in tanks for food production can yield, under favourable conditions, about 17 tons of dry algae per acre. Tests on algae growing in sewage have given yields as high as 36 tons per acre. The potential value of the process is shown by these figures.

Although we do not as yet nourish ourselves on microscopic algae directly, we do so indirectly whenever we eat fish. The food of fishes all comes, directly or indirectly, from the microscopic phytoplankton of the sea. Many fish and other marine animals are plankton eaters, and a plankton-fed animal does not necessarily have to be small. The blue whale, the largest animal that has ever lived on earth, feeds in this way; instead of teeth it has in its mouth sheets of whalebone which form an efficient filter, and these strain the planktonic organisms out of the sea water in such numbers that a blue whale 100 feet long and weighing nearly 150 tons can find all the nourishment it needs. It is true that the plankton includes such things as jellyfish, small crustaceans and the like, but these animals were nourished on phytoplankton.

Even where a fish does not take phytoplankton directly it nevertheless feeds upon it indirectly. The herring, for instance, feeds mainly on copepods, but these animals in turn feed upon phytoplankton. Either directly, therefore, or through food chains like that of the herring, the phytoplankton is responsible for all life in the sea.

The use of seaweed as a manure for land goes back to before the dawn of history, though it is surprising that, in spite of the fact that Britain possesses a wealth of seaweed on her rocky shores, it is not more greatly used. Perhaps one reason is the cost and inconvenience of carting it from the shore to the land, especially when we consider the amount of wet weight there is in even a little seaweed. The farmers of western coastal districts, however, have always been alive to its value, and for centuries seaweed collection has been a regular part of the routine.

Seaweed is an excellent manure; it contains about as much nitrogen as an equal weight of farmyard manure and about twice as much potash. This makes it very suitable for soils lacking in potash, and in particular the lighter sandy soils, which also benefit from the effect the gelatinous nature of the seaweed has in improving its water-holding capacity. Nitrogen in seaweed is not quickly available to plants, so that seaweed manure acts rather slowly. It is rather low in phosphorus content, so needs to be supplemented with bone meal or some other phosphatic fertilizer. It is rich in trace elements—those elements that, though essential for plant growth, are needed only in minute amounts—and its effect on the physical properties of the soil is excellent.

The best way to use seaweed as a manure is to plough it in while fresh, but if this is not practicable or desirable, it can be allowed to rot on the surface of the soil, or it can be composted with or without other organic material. Seaweed makes excellent compost, and this aspect of its use might be more widely exploited.

Seaweed always contains some common salt from the sea,

but this is not usually a disadvantage. Indeed, certain crops, such as mangolds, swedes, cabbages, and asparagus, grow all the better for it.

Seaweeds belonging to the Corallinaceae, such as *Lithothamnion*, contain a great deal of lime in their thalli, and in places where they are particularly abundant, as in parts of the west coast, they have given rise to what are known as 'coral sands', which may contain anything from 40 to 80 per cent of lime. These coral sands are found in Connemara, in Cornwall and in the Hebrides, and are used to provide dressings of lime for use on acid soils.

The first seaweed industry to develop was the 'kelp' trade. This is now virtually obsolete, but at one time it was a very flourishing business. In the Scilly Isles, kelp burning was the islanders' sole industry (apart from wrecking and smuggling) from 1684 until well into the nineteenth century. Originally the word 'kelp' was used to describe the burnt ash of the brown seaweeds, later being used for the seaweeds themselves. This ash was found to contain a great deal of soda, and so it became customary to use it in the manufacture of glass, replacing the substance, known as 'barilla', obtained from the ash of the glasswort (*Salicornia*). The French were the first to use kelp in this way, but the habit soon spread to the rest of Europe, and by about 1720 the kelp industry was firmly entrenched both in Ireland and Scotland.

The history of the kelp industry is one of ups and downs. Initially, it was used purely as a source of soda, the algae mainly used being species of *Laminaria* and *Fucus*, together with *Ascophyllum nodosum*. The weeds were first allowed to dry, after which they were burned in kilns. Burning was continued until a cake of ash was formed, from 15 to 24 inches thick. As in those days the iodine in the weed was neglected, the temperature of the burning was of no importance; later, when the iodine became the valuable product rather than the soda, it had to be carefully controlled. On the whole, *Fucus* and *Ascophyllum* were preferred to *Laminaria*, because they were richer in soda.

During the American War of Independence, and again during

the Peninsular War, the kelp trade boomed extensively, but a few years later, in 1825, the duty on imported barilla was reduced, and, at the same time, the salt tax was removed. As salt was a secondary product of the production of soda, both these had a disastrous effect on the kelp trade and almost put a stop to it. However, it took a new lease of life when the French kelp burners, in the process of extracting potassium carbonate, discovered that their kelp was rich in iodine. This immediately revitalized the industry, especially in Scotland, and many factories sprang up almost overnight for the production of iodine. With the new product came a new outlook upon the weeds; *Laminaria* was now preferred to *Fucus* and *Ascophyllum* because of its greater iodine content. This revival in the kelp trade lasted until the discovery of beds of saltpetre in Chile, from which iodine was produced much more cheaply than from kelp; this dealt the industry a staggering blow, and when a little later great deposits of common salt were found at Stassfurt in Germany, providing raw material for producing soda at a fraction of its former cost, the industry finally succumbed to the inevitable.

Iodine is still manufactured from kelp in Japan, where *Laminaria*, *Ecklonia* and *Eisenia* are mostly used; about 100 tons of iodine are produced yearly, constituting about 5 to 7 per cent of the world's supply.

On the Pacific coast of South America and Canada kelp burning was started in 1910 for a different reason. The giant kelps *Macrocystis*, *Nereocystis* and *Alaria* contain a great deal of potash; *Nereocystis* contains about 19 per cent—an extraordinary instance of the accumulation of a substance that is present in the surrounding medium only in small amounts. When America began to have difficulties in getting German supplies of potash, she turned to her kelps. The seaweeds were cut under water and the cut weed was transferred to barges by conveyor belt; it was then dried in a revolving drier, and treated for the recovery of potash. This version of the seaweed industry flourished for a time, but eventually it went the way of the kelp trade in Europe.

The modern kelp industry is very different from the old. In 1883 E. C. Stanford discovered that many of the brown seaweeds yielded a sticky substance which, treated with sodium carbonate and then with a mineral acid, gave a compound which was new to science. This was called alginic acid. At the time alginic acid was no more than a scientific curiosity, but in 1934 it was discovered that it had a use in preparing transparent wrapping paper, and a company was formed for its extraction from seaweed. That, however, was only the beginning. Since then, this useful compound has been found to be a kind of industrial jack-of-all-trades, and no doubt many more uses for it have yet to be discovered.

Alginic acid, or algin, is a compound of d–mannuronic acid, and the amount found in the various seaweeds used as a source for it varies from 15 to 40 per cent. Processes for its extraction vary, but most of them depend upon extracting the weed with acid, followed by treatment with a sodium carbonate solution. Algin itself is insoluble in water, but some of its salts, such as sodium alginate, are readily soluble. The sodium salt dissolves in water to give a viscous solution which can be spun into artificial silk. These artificial silks are soluble in sodium carbonate, and are used in what is called the 'disappearing fibre' technique in weaving. The alginate fibre is mixed with other fibres, and after weaving the alginate fibre can be dissolved out. If threads that are resistant to solution are required, they can be obtained by replacing the sodium or calcium in the soluble thread with chromium or beryllium. Usually the yarn is woven in the form of calcium alginate, and then placed in a solution of chromium or beryllium acetate; replacement then takes place spontaneously.

Alginates have many other uses besides making artificial fibres. Sodium alginate is used extensively as a stabilizer for ice cream, both in this country and in America, and it is also used for the preparation of soups and sauces, and in wrapped cakes to keep them moist. Alginates are also used in the pharmaceutical and cosmetic industries. Gauze containing calcium alginate is useful for preventing bleeding; calcium alginate gauze is used in various forms of dressings. Alginates are also used for the preparation of plastic for taking dental impressions. Recent experiments have been carried out on alginates as improvers of the soil, and they are likely in the future to oust such materials as krillium. We are probably as yet only beginning to discover the range of usefulness of the alginates.

Another important use for seaweeds today is in the production of agar-agar. This is used extensively for culturing bacteria and fungi in the laboratory, for it provides a medium that will set to a jelly, and is not attacked, as gelatine often is, by the organisms growing on it. Agar is the calcium or magnesium salt of the sulphuric acid ester of a short chain of galactose molecules. Besides being used as a culture medium for micro-organisms, it can be employed for a number of other purposes, including the sizing of fabrics, the canning of fish, the manufacture of paper and glue, the finishing of leather goods, the preparation of medicines and cosmetics, and the thickening of ice cream.

Before 1939 the world's supply of agar came from Japan, the alga mainly used being *Gelidium amansii*. About 2,000 tons of agar were produced every year. With the outbreak of war supplies of agar were cut off, and the various countries of the Western world had to look for alternative sources of supply. This led to the use of various seaweeds that had not previously been thought of as agar producers, and each country tended to develop the species that grew locally; thus, Great Britain used *Gigartina stellata* and *Chondrus crispus*, America used *Gelidium cartilaginium*, *Gracilaria confervoides* and *Hypnea musiformis*, and so on. The method of collection depended on the habit of the weed; usually they were hand-picked from the rocks, but for *Gracilaria* and *Hypnea* nets were used, and the Australian *Gracilaria confervoides* was brought up by a trawl, as it lived in relatively deep water.

In Japan they obtain a form of glue called funorin from the red seaweed *Gloeopeltis furcata*. The alga is cultivated for this purpose by raising the shore to a suitable level for its growth.

Diatomaceous earth or kieselguhr—the deposits of fossil diatoms found in various parts of the world—is an important article of commerce, and is used for an increasing variety of purposes. Its traditional use was as an abrasive in silver polishes and tooth pastes, and it was also formerly used for absorbing nitro-glycerine to make dynamite, a much safer explosive that can be transported without the fear of premature explosion. Today, about three-fifths of the world production of kieselguhr is used as a packing for filters for straining liquids, especially in the sugar industry. It is also used as an inert filler for various things, including paint, and as an insulator for blast furnaces and other very hot objects. At temperatures exceeding 1,000°C kieselguhr is preferable to asbestos, as it does not shrink and it retains its insulating powers even at a red heat.

Deposits of diatomaceous earth had their origin in water, either fresh or marine. Some deposits are of great extent. The largest so far known is at Lompoc, California, where the deposits are over 700 feet thick and extend for miles. The thickest is in the Santa Maria oilfield, California, where the subterranean deposits reach a thickness of 3,000 feet.

If we were to include the uses of lichens with those of the algae, this brief list could be extended a great deal; an account of the uses of lichens is given in Chapter 6. In fairness to the fungi, however, it must be admitted that the useful products that the lichens produce stem from the fungi rather than their algal partners, important though the latter may be in the general organization of the lichen.

I think enough has been said in this chapter to indicate that the algae as a whole are worthy of better things than to be written off as 'something of a nuisance'.

Glossary

Terms used only once in the text have, in the main, been omitted from the Glossary.

Akinete. A non-motile spore formed by some of the blue-green algae.

Alternation of generations. The alternation of a spore-bearing generation with a generation that bears sex organs.

Antheridium. The male sex organ of algae and fungi.

Aplanospore. A general term for a non-motile spore.

Auxiliary cell. The cell that receives the fertilized egg nucleus in many of the red algae.

Auxospore. A type of spore formed in the diatoms which results in the restoration of the organism to its original size.

Carpogonium. The female sex organ of red algae.

Carpospore. A spore formed by the red algae on the ends of gonimoblast filaments, subsequently to fertilization.

Carposporophyte. The generation in the red algae that produces the carpospores.

Chromatic adaptation. The development of pigment in algae of a different colour from chlorophyll, assisting photosynthesis in blue-green light.

Conceptacle. The cavity in which the sex organs are formed in *Fucus* and its allies.

Contractile vacuole. A vacuole which, by expansion and contraction, pumps water out of a cell.

Cyanophycean starch. The carbohydrate which, in the blue-green algae, serves as a reserve of food.

Cyanophycin granules. Granules, probably of protein, which occur in the protoplasm of the blue-green algae.

198

Diploid. Having the double number of chromosomes, characteristic of the sporophyte generation in plants.

Endospore. A type of spore formed by some of the blue-green algae, in which the contents of a cell divide up into a large number of small spores.

Epiphloeophyte. An alga that inhabits the bark of trees.

Epiphyte. A plant that grows on another one, without any organic connexion with it.

Epitheca. The top half of the frustule of a diatom.

Flagellum. A hair-like projection of protoplasm by the waving movement of which a one-celled organism is able to swim.

Frustule. The silicious outer case of a diatom.

Fucosan. The material, thought to be allied to tannin, found in the fucosan vesicles in the protoplasm of brown algae.

Fucoxanthin. The brown pigment found in the brown algae.

Gametangium. The organ in which the gametes are formed.

Gamete. A male or female sex cell.

Gametophyte. The generation in the life history of a plant which bears the sex organs.

Girdle. The sides of the frustule of a diatom. Also, the groove in which the transverse flagellum of a dinoflagellate is situated.

Gonimoblast filaments. The filaments which, in most red algae, bear the carpospores.

Haploid. Having the single number of chromosomes, characteristic of the gametophyte generation in plants.

Heterocyst. A large cell with transparent contents that, in filamentous blue-green algae, is often associated with the breaking of the filament into hormogonia.

Heteromorphic alternation of generations. An alternation of generations in which the sporophyte differs markedly from the gametophyte.

Heterotrichous filament. The body of a filamentous alga in which one can distinguish between a prostrate filament and erect branches.

Hormogonia. The portions into which a filamentous blue-green alga breaks up on reproduction.

Hypotheca. The lower part of the frustule of a diatom.

Isomorphic alternation of generations. An alternation of generations in which the sporophyte resembles the gametophyte closely.

Lithophyte. A plant that grows on rocks.

Littoral zone. That part of the seashore that lies between the tide marks.

Macrandrous. Term applied to a species of *Oedogonium* that does not have special dwarf male plants in its life history.

Meiosis. A form of division of the nucleus of a cell that results in a halving of the number of chromosomes.

Mitosis. The normal process of division of the nucleus of a cell that results in splitting of the chromosomes and their equal sharing between the two daughter cells.

Mycobiont. The fungal partner in a lichen.

Nannandrous. Term applied to a species of *Oedogonium* that has special dwarf male plants in its life history.

Oöblast. A tubular outgrowth from the base of the carpogonium in certain red algae, through which the zygote nucleus, or its derivatives, pass into the auxiliary cell.

Oogonium. The female sex organ in algae and fungi.

Oospore. A spore formed from a fertilized egg cell.

Ostiole. The opening by which the conceptacle of a member of the Fucales connects with the exterior.

Paramylum. The starch-like reserve food formed by members of the Euglenophyta.

Parthenogenesis. The development of an egg into an embryo without fertilization.

Phycobiont. The algal partner in a lichen.

Phycocyanin. The characteristic blue-green pigment of the Rhodophyta and Cyanophyta.

Phycoerythrin. The characteristic red pigment of the Rhodophyta and Cyanophyta.

Phytoplankton. Those members of the plankton that are plant-like.

Plankton. A general term for those organisms, animal and plant, that float freely in water.

Pusule. A large vacuole in the cell of a dinoflagellate.

Pyrenoid. A crystalline body situated in the chloroplast of an alga, which appears to be connected in some way with starch formation.

Raphe. The groove running longitudinally down the centre of the frustule of a pennate diatom.

Rhizinae. The hair-like processes by which many lichens are fixed to the substratum.

Soma. The vegetative part of a plant body, as opposed to the part that is concerned in reproduction.

Spermatium. The male gamete of a red alga.

Sporophyte. The generation in the life history of a plant that bears the asexual spores.

Sulcus. The groove in which the longitudinal flagellum of a dinoflagellate is situated.

Supporting cell. The cell that bears the carpogonium in one of the red algae.

Symbiosis. A phenomenon in which one organism lives in another for mutual benefit.

Tetrasporophyte. The generation in many red algae that bears special spores called tetraspores.

Thallus. A plant body which is not divided into stem, root and leaf.

Theca. The cellulose shell in which the cell of a dinoflagellate is enclosed.

Thermophilic algae. Algae that inhabit hot surroundings, such as hot springs.

Trichogyne. The trunk-like extension of the carpogonium of a red alga on which the spermatia settle.

Trichome. A single row of cells in a filament of one of the blue-green algae.

Valve. The top or bottom of the frustule in a diatom.

Zonation. The arrangement of different species of seaweeds in a number of different belts or zones on the seashore.

Zygospore. A spore formed in the course of sexual reproduction where the female gamete is not differentiated as an egg cell.

Zygote. The cell formed by the fusion of two gametes.

Index

203

INDEX

Gonyaulax catenella, 100; G. polyedra, 100
Gonium, 37–38; G. pectorale, 37
Gracilaria confervoides, 196; G. verrucosa, 138
green laver, 52
guanine, 44
Gymnodinium, 100; G. brevis, 169–70

Halicystis, 158
Heterocapso, 100
heterocysts, 148
heterotrichous filament, 58
hijiki, 187
Hijikia fusiforme, 187
Himanthalia elongata, 122
Hofmeister cycle, 108
Holosteum umbellatum, 159
Holy Loch, 161
hormogonia, 147, 148
horned wrack, 118
Huxley, T. H., 22
Hydra, 185
Hydrodictyon, 67, 158, 172; H. reticulatum, 67, 172
hydrogen sulphide, as hydrogen donor in photosynthesis, 154
Hypnea musiformis, 196

Iceland moss, 81
iodine, in seaweeds, 17–18, 158–9, 187–8, 193–4
iodovolatization, 158
Irish moss, 137, 187
isidia, 71, 72

Jania rubens, 136
jelly-fish, 82

kelp, 104, 112–17, 157
kelp trade, 17–18, 158, 193–6
knotted wrack, 122 (see also Ascophyllum nodosum)
kombu, 187

Laminaria, 18, 104, 105, 112–16, 119, 122, 156, 157, 158, 179, 187,

193–4; L. digitata, 112–13, 179; L. hyperborea, 113; L. saccharina, 113–14
laver bread, 126, 187
Lecanora conizeoides, 79; L. esculentia, 81
Lemanea, 172
Letharia vulpina, 81
lichens, 14, 17, 66, 69–86, 184, 197
Lithophyllum encrustans, 136–7
Lithothamnion, 193; L. lenormandi, 136–7
litmus, 80

Macrocystis, 15, 104, 112, 115, 116, 117, 157, 194; M. pyrifera, 117, 162
manna, 81
may weed, 112
meiosis, 46, 99, 106, 111, 115, 120, 133, 144
mercury, accumulation by Holosteum umbellatum, 159
meristoderm, 119
mermaid's tresses, 21
Mesophyllum lichenoides, 136
metabolic movements, of Euglena, 89
Microcoleus, 183
Microcystis, 166, 171
Mimosa pudica, 87–88
mitosis, 46
monoaxial thallus, 129
motility, of diatoms, 94, 95
Mougeotia, 28–29
multiaxial thallus, 129–30

nannandrous species of Oedogonium, 57–58
nannoplankton, 181
Nemalion elminthoides, 131–3
Nereocystis, 112, 115, 157, 161, 194; N. luetkiana, 117
Nitella, 157
Noctiluca, 82, 85
Nostoc, 20, 70, 73–74, 145, 162, 184, 187

Ochrolechia tartarea, 80

205